Neurobehavioral
and Perceptual Dysfunction
in Learning Disabled Children

Neurobehavioral and Perceptual Dysfunction in Learning Disabled Children

by

Delmont C. Morrison

Langley Porter Psychiatric Institute
University of California, San Francisco

C. J. Hogrefe, Inc.
Lewiston, NY · Toronto

Canadian Cataloguing in Publication Data

Morrison, Delmont C., 1932–
Neurobehavioral and perceptual dysfunction
in learning disabled children

Bibliography: p.
Includes indexes.
ISBN 0-88937-014-1

1. Perceptually handicapped children. 2. Developmentally disabled children. 3. Learning–Physiological aspects. I. Title.

RJ496.L4M67   1985   618.92'8   C85-098841-1

Library of Congress Cataloging in Publication Data

Morrison, Delmont C., 1932–
Neurobehavioral and perceptual dysfunction
in learning disabled children

Bibliography: p.
Includes index.
1. Learning disabilities. 2. Perception, Disorders of. 3. Central nervous system–Diseases–Complications and sequalae. 4. Perceptually handicapped children. I. Title. [DNLM: 1. Central Nervous System–physiopathology. 2. Central Nervous System Diseases–in infancy & childhood. 3. Learning Disorders. 4. Perceptual Disorders. WS 110 M878n]

RJ506.L4M67   1985   618.92'855   85-8656
ISBN 0-88937-014-1

C. J. Hogrefe, Inc.
P. O. Box 51
Lewiston, NY 14092

Canadian edition published by
C. J. Hogrefe, Inc.
12 Bruce Park Ave.
Toronto, Ontario M4P 2S3

Printed in Germany

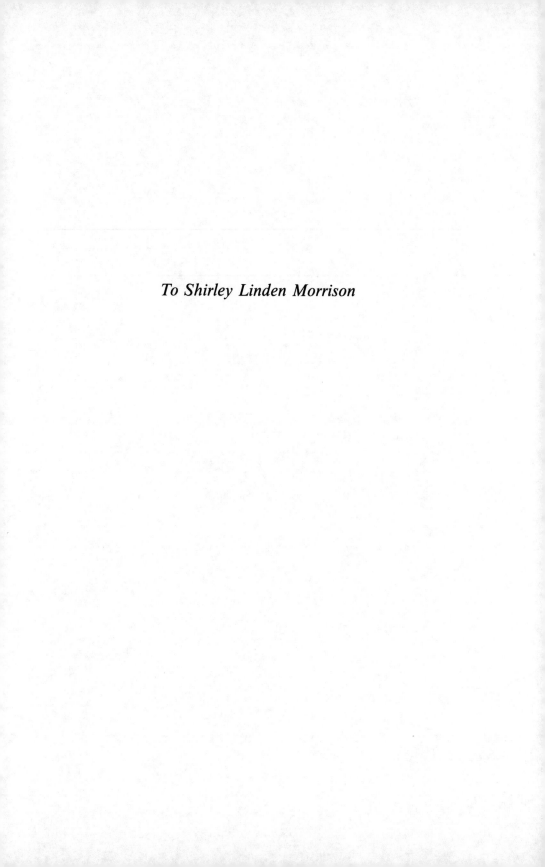

To Shirley Linden Morrison

Acknowledgements

A number of individuals have contributed to the writing of this text. Two former students, Nancy Byl and Stephen Hinshaw, have stimulated my thinking on the subjects of neurobehavioral dysfunction and learning disabilities. I am particularly indebted to Patricia Pothier who first introduced me to this special area. Lois Herman and Steven Friedlander both contributed significantly to the first efforts to quantify the clinical evaluation of these subtle signs of dysfunction. My friends and colleagues at the CHILD Center in Kentfield, California, Win Setrakian, Estol Carte, Judy Allen and Jean Sublett, have contributed in various ways to my professional growth and development. It has been a pleasure to work with them. Vernnez Rockett and Lauren Mezey were of great help in getting my words on the printed page and their expertise with the word processor made the writing of the text less of a burden. I thank them sincerely. Mary Prusmack's illustrations of children add significantly to the quality of the text. A good deal of the research reported here that bears this author's name was supported by grants from the Babcock Memorial Endowment, the San Francisco Foundation, and the Dominican College Learning Disabilities Project. Finally, I wish to acknowledge the time, encouragement, and willing consultation provided me over the years by Shirley Linden Morrison. I have been fortunate and privileged to have such support.

Delmont C. Morrison
February 1985

Contents

Contents

Chapter 1

Overview

Introduction

This text will focus on a particular group of children. In their developmental history they have not experienced demonstrable central nervous system disease or injury. However, when evaluated objectively they demonstrate positive signs of neurobehavioral dysfunction, such as the presence of tonic neck reflexes, inadequate postural and equilibrium reactions, and related abnormalities of the vestibular system. Because the assessment techniques used to evaluate neurobehavioral dysfunction (NBD) are seldom used in a standard neurological examination, most of these children would not have been noted as pathological when assessed by a neurologist, although some neurologists may have noted the occurrence of "soft" signs. Another major characteristic of this population is that their intelligence is average or better and they demonstrate a high incidence of perceptual processing problems, learning disabilities, and related behavioral problems. Although the data must be considered cautiously, there are indications that this population constitutes approximately one quarter of the children found in special classes for the learning disabled. Given a standard neurological evaluation, these children would not demonstrate the medically accepted signs of neurological pathology. However, the signs of NBD that they frequently show, such as the tonic neck reflexes, are known to occur in more pronounced form in children with CNS pathology, such as cerebral palsy. Evidence suggests that these signs in children with learning disabilities indicate CNS dysfunction of a more subtle type than that related to a known history of significant injury or disease. The occurrence of these signs in children with learning disabilities has been considered as evidence that these more subtle indications of dysfunction contribute to the individual child's perceptual processing problems that are the basis of the learning disability. From the assessment of these dysfunctions, therapists evolve programs of intervention that address these dysfunctions, and in some cases, the related perceptual processing problems rather than the cognitive problem, such as reading retardation.

The term neurobehavioral dysfunction is used in this text to describe the various signs that appear to occur in clusters rather than in isolation when these children are assessed. It is unclear whether or not these frequently occurring clusters appear in predictable patterns and should be described as a syndrome, as the term is used in medicine. The word neurobehavioral is used because it reflects two working assumptions. One is that the techniques of assessment that have most clinical research value are behavioral. This behavior is public, observable, and quantifiable. The other assumption is that an underlying neurological abnormality is the basis of the observed deviation in behavior. However, the actual data describing this abnormal neurological substrate in terms of either etiology or current dysfunction in the children of interest in this text is simply unknown. As a result of this, the focus of the evaluation is much more on behavior viewed in a developmental context. The occurrence or non-occurrence of these signs of NBD within the framework of a sequence of development is crucial in classifying them as deviant or simply as normal variation. In terms of measurement, for these signs to be considered deviant, they must occur less frequently and/or to a lesser degree in children having no academic problems when compared to the subsample of the population of children with learning disabilities that is of interest in this text. However, it is the lack of inhibition in the primitive reflexes *and* the retarded development of the postural and equilibrium reactions that is the major characteristic discriminating these children from children in general and within the population of LD children. The persistent occurrence of the reflexes and inadequate body reactions to position change reflect a major disruption in the normal developmental process not experienced by other children. This disruption in development is closely related to a particular pattern of perceptual dysfunctions and problems in attention and concentration.

While NBD contributes to a failure in sensory-motor integration and a corresponding undifferentiated body image and lowered self-esteem, the perceptual dysfunction contributes directly to the child's failure to acquire the automatized perceptual skills necessary for the acquisition of writing and reading during the elementary school years. The major perceptual dysfunctions characteristic of this group occur in visual tracking, pursuit, and sequencing. All of these are functions of ocular-motor control. Ocular-motor control itself is

2

influenced by the vestibular system which is significantly dysfunctional in these LD children. These are chronic dysfunctions that impede perceptual learning and result in the early development of deficits in attention and concentration. It is important to note that the impaired sensory integration and perceptual dysfunctions result in a failure to learn prior to school experience. However, this learning disability is usually not detected until the child must perceive and integrate visual auditory stimulus for academic learning and performance.

The Child of Concern

This child's development is characterized by subtle deviances from developmentally normal children soon after birth. Because of underutilization of obstetric and pediatric service, as well as interrelated issues of pre- and postnatal nutrition, this child may be found more frequently in some minority races and lower social economic status (SES) groups. However, it is not clear how frequently this occurs and the child is found frequently enough in middle and upper SES families independent of race. As is true of all infants, this infant responds to body on body changes and shifts in the relationship of the body to gravity by a series of clearly defined and predictable reflexes. In the normal course of events these reflexes become adaptively inhibited and integrated into the ongoing fine and gross motor development so that when the child begins to sit up and crawl these reflexes contribute to this development rather than disrupt the process. As the reflexes become less dominant, postural and equilibrium reactions serve to automatically adjust the child's body to these new relationships to gravity, space, and motion.

It is probably at this time that the subtle deviancy from normal development begins. Because there is considerable variation in sensory-motor development that is considered normal during the period between birth to two years, this child's particular pattern may not attract attention. For example, although there may be slight but consistent delays in sitting, crawling, walking, and eye-hand coordination, all these developmental landmarks will be obtained. An experienced adult observer may think the child is slightly awkward or excitable but not that different from many children. This is due in part to the fact that one of the more noticeable developmental landmarks, language acquisition, will not be delayed and may be accelerated.

3

However, closer examination of the child would demonstrate that three interrelated variations in development have occurred: (1) a number of primitive reflexes, particularly the tonic neck reflexes, have not been adequately inhibited, (2) postural and equilibrium reactions are inadequate and the child's adjustments to gravity are not automatic, (3) ocular-motor control and visual perception during motion is unstable and visual-motor integration inadequate.

Certainly the major task for the developing child is to obtain adequate information regarding the environment. There are many ways that this process occurs but two of the major means, active perceptual-motor exploration and visual perception, will not produce reliable information for the child having neurobehavioral and perceptual dysfunction. This is particularly unfortunate because knowledge of the world during this time is unique in that it is greatly influenced by sensorimotor intelligence and preoperational thought (Piaget, 1954). These first ways of knowing the environment provide a basis for later evolving operational thought and both sensorimotor intelligence and preoperational thought can be negatively influenced by neurobehavioral and perceptual dysfunctions. The period of sensorimotor intelligence is characterized by the child's use of the primary, secondary, and tertiary circular reactions as a means of exploring the physical environment and obtaining reliable information about it. Novelty first attracts attention and maintains concentration until the child knows the object or event at a sensory-motor level. In time, between approximately 10-18 months, the child creates novelty and subordinates action to fit particular aspects of objects and relationships among objects in the environment. These circular reactions, as well as the child's developing perception, contribute to the first relatively stable schemas the child has of objects, space, time, motion and causal relationships.

The circular reactions can only provide useful information if there is a significant correspondence between what the child perceives and does motorically and environmental feedback. Accumulated sensorimotor intelligence at one stage is necessary for the transition to the next stage. Reflexes provide limited information regarding the environment, but the child must have a stable reflex system for the circular reactions to develop. The failure to adequately inhibit the tonic neck reflexes will limit information available to the child in any situation requiring coordinated movement of the head, legs, arms, and hands. Unlike children with moderate to severe cerebral palsy who experience a pronounced disruption in this activity, the child with sensory

4

and perceptual dysfunction experiences a more subtle lack of corre-spondence between action and feedback. The data base accumulated is more variable and inaccurate rather than one of an absolute low frequency with no data in some areas. Piaget notes that the develop-ment of visually guided prehension is of major importance in terms of expanding sensory-motor and perceptual knowledge of the environ-ment (Piaget, 1952, p. 121). The tonic neck reflexes would impede this development but the inadequate ocular-motor responses would also have a negative effect. Automatic nystagmus movements compen-sate for the changing relationship between the environment and the child in motion so that stable visual information is available. This vestibular function contributes to the child's adaptations to the envir-onment as gross motor activities such as crawling, walking, and run-ning develop. Again, the child with NBD and perceptual dysfunc-tions will show subtle, but significant, inadequacies in activities that require automatic adjustments to changes in gravity in general, but specifically when the task requires coordination of the body while in motion and responding to a moving or stable object. The most com-mon example of this is the child who cannot run and catch or kick a stable or moving ball with accuracy. An example of a more subtle problem is the six- or seven-year old who moves his or her head as he/she tries to read or write a sequence of letters or words. It will take this child much longer to do either task and the production will be inaccurate when compared to developmentally normal children.

There are at least three implications for future learning in this early occurring deviancy in development. The first of these relates to the fact that the next major stage of development, the preoperational period, is characterized by important interactions between perception and cognition. The child at risk for developing later academic prob-lems will enter the stage of preoperational thought with an unstable and poorly articulated sensorimotor intelligence. The sensorimotor representations of objects, causality, space and time will be undiffer-entiated. Representational thought developing during the preopera-tional period is greatly influenced by perception (Piaget, 1962, 1979). Preoperational thought is dominant at a critical age range beginning at approximately age 2 and extending through age 7. The child in kindergarten and the first and second grades will be be greatly influ-enced by perception in his or her adaptations to academic learning. Normal perception in children at this time will result in nonadaptive responses to problems and children with perceptual dysfunctions will have even greater misinformation regarding the world. Representa-

5

tions during this time are formed by information gained by perception rather than active operational systems of thought. The child's knowledge of the world is based on the most dominant perceptual features in an experience as well as an inability to gain information from observed transformations rather than end states. Based on the linear quality of perceptual information, the child has difficulty in imagining that a process could be reversed. Representations of preoperational concepts of the world are unstable, and from an adult's perspective, illogical. However, this perceptual thought is more stable than sensorimotor intelligence and is the framework for the development of knowledge of the world based on thought organized by concrete and formal operations.

The disruption in development caused by sensory and perceptual dysfunction may result in a child experiencing an extended period of preoperational thought. However, the child may compensate for difficulties at this level by using more language-oriented operational systems of representing the world that are based on imitation and identification with adults or older children. This is the child who dislikes athletics, does poorly on visual-motor tasks but has strong verbal-social skills. He or she may not be able to read well but may have an extensive vocabulary. These are the more adaptive responses to the stress experienced. The second implication for the developmental process for a child with sensory and perceptual dysfunction is the range of adaptive and non-adaptive emotional and behavioral responses to the anxiety and frustration experienced in learning. Any child with a learning disability is at-risk for developing behavior problems. For many of those children whose failure to learn is related to a more cognitive dysfunction, the behavior problems may not occur until the child must acquire reading comprehension. The child with problems in sensory integration and perception may arrive in kindergarten with problems in attention and concentration. Repeated failure, performing below expectancy and finding no adequate way to learn at the preacademic level may result in restless behavior or as it is labeled more formally: hyperactivity, with or without attention deficit disorder.

The third implication is the failure to develop automatized functions at both the levels of sensory and perceptual integration. Automatized behaviors are ones which have been so highly practiced as to require a minimum of conscious attention and concentration for their efficient execution (Boverman, Boverman & Kaiber, 1966). During the period of acquisition, a great deal of conscious effort is given to

6

the details of the task to be learned, but over time, little attention and concentration are needed for the details because the behaviors are automatic. The behavior occurs daily and includes walking, talking, reading, writing and maintaining perceptual constancies. Children with problems in sensory and perceptual integration frequently fail to develop automatized functions in all these areas. As the child begins to walk and run, conscious manipulation of attention to the various components of the act and gravity is common for all children. However, in a relatively short period of time, most children walk and run automatically and shift conscious attention to variations of these activities, such as running and kicking a ball. One of the major adaptive functions of automatization is that conscious attention to variations of these activities is freed to be used to elaborate on motor activities or to perceive spatial-temporal relationships. In adaptive perception automatized functions serve to organize the components of the perceptual information available. This level of organization is basic for preoperational thought. Preoperational thought is limited by the restricted range of information available to the child at that level of conceptual organization. However, once this source of information is stable the child can shift attention to cues in the perceptual experience that are potential sources of information for concrete operational thought. For example, a series of perceptual events preceding an end state are recorded automatically and transformed cognitively from predictable perceptual events to cues of transformations leading to end states. Being able to perceive all the information available automatically is basic to being able to use attention and concentration to form alternative cognitive representations and interpretations of events.

Sensory and Perceptual Integration and Reading Acquisition

One of the characteristics of the unimpaired reader is that the perceptual component of reading is done automatically. This reader is unaware of this component and is free to devote attention and concentration to comprehending the content of what is being read. The perceptual component of reading is automatized unless a new or difficult word is encountered or the competent reader in one language begins to learn to read in a new language. During such situations the shift in attention and concentration to the perceptual components is dramatic. The reading-retarded child frequently never develops the various perceptual components of the reading task, particularly the sequencing of perceptual data, to the automatic level. This reader has less attention and concentration to give to comprehension because the perceptual component is not automatized. The child with problems in sensory and perceptual integration encounters difficulty learning how to read because the acquisition of reading between the ages of six to eight is a perceptual process that is dependent on a stable perceptual organization that does not exist in this child.

During the execution of a complex skill, such as reading, it is necessary to coordinate many component processes within a relatively short period of time. If any one of these components requires a significant amount of attention, reading performance will be impaired. An individual's capacity for attention is limited. If the individual's capacity is exceeded because components are not adequately mastered and automatized, the end goal of reading, that is adequate comprehension of content, will not be obtained. An understanding of a complex skill such as reading can be obtained by an evaluation of how the various component subskills of the process have been automatized (LaBerge & Samuels, 1974). The transformation of written stimuli into meaning involves a sequence of stages in information processing. The first step in this process for the child beginning to learn how to read is the construction of visual codes which includes perception of multidirectional lines that become letters, relationships between letters that become words and relationships between words themselves. Incoming information from the page is perceived in terms of lines, angles, intersections, etc. This graphemic information is analyzed for particular features that transform them into letter codes. These codes serve as spelling patterns which in turn contribute into word codes and word group codes.

During this stage, attention is expended on learning these perceptual codes. Once this component is mastered and automatic, attention is no longer needed to the degree that it was needed during acquisition. During perceptual learning, selection of relevant features requires attention as the child learns to discriminate the relevant perceptual cues. After the child has experienced several discrimination tasks, he or she develops learning strategies that permit faster acquisition rates. This allows more attention to be freed than was true during the earlier trial and error efforts. At first individual bits of information are processed but eventually units of perceptual data become transformed into words. An analysis of the perceptual learning com-

8

ponent of reading would have to include the acquisition of visual-auditory perceptions that are transformed into meaningful words. The major point is that the perceptual component of reading skills is the first one that must be acquired to the level that it is automatized or the limited amount of attention the child has cannot be shifted to the other more cognitive components such as association learning and higher order linguistic operations. Because of sensory and perceptual dysfunctions the NBD child cannot maintain a consistent perceptual base either in decoding a single visual stimulus or a sequence of visual stimuli into graphemes and words. He or she may not have problems in decoding a sequence of words presented through the auditory channel but would have difficulty integrating visual-auditory information presented in a sequence. Consequently these basic perceptual components are never adequately automatized in the act of reading and the limited attention available is not sufficiently freed to enable the child to acquire the more advanced components of reading at the expected level.

Chapter 2

Neurobehavioral Dysfunction: Empirical Basis

Introduction

Although assessment of NBD has only recently been applied with LD children, many of the assessment procedures have been in existence for some time. Interestingly enough, in terms of the role of neuropathology in learning disabilities, early signs of deviation in reflexes and reactions have been used by pediatricians to detect infants at risk. Equally interesting, in the same regard, is the fact that the techniques are routinely used to diagnose cerebral palsy in infancy and early childhood. Some awareness of the clinical data regarding the occurrence of these signs in other pathological conditions is needed to understand their possible contribution to the development of learning disabilties.

Primitive Reflexes and Postural Adjustments

It is clear that one of the first developmental tasks of the infant is to adapt to the force of gravity. There is considerable evidence that infants independent of culture do this in a fairly predictable sequence (Gesell, 1940). However, there is also evidence that particular variations in environment, such as deprivation (Hunt, 1964) or neuropathology (Bobath, 1971) or the interaction of the two, can significantly affect this sequence. Major milestones in this sequence, such as moving from crawling to walking, are important in terms of adaptation to gravity, but have added significance in that they enable the infant to explore and acquire a greater range of experience and consequent cognitive growth. NBD does not appear to be acquired after birth, so

11

it is assumed to be a contributing factor to the infant's earliest adaptations to gravity.

Although the motor sequence is significantly influenced by maturation and appears to be relatively automatic, closer examination indicates that there is a crucial and complex hierarchy of reflexes and automatic movement patterns that provide the basis for coordinated motor performance (Sherrington, 1961). Clinical observation (Hellebrandt et al., 1956; Waterland, 1967) and research (Walters, 1967) indicate that the nervous system is programmed to respond to stimuli with simple as well as more complex movements observable as motor patterns that lack refinement and have limited adaptability. These automatic reactions exert a continuous influence on muscle tone, posture, and movement, serving the development of coordinated voluntary motor performance that is characterized by a broader range of complex adaptive patterns closely related to environmental stimulation. A host of these basic automatic functions are related to the vestibular-proprioceptive systems that influence muscle tone, equilibrium and ocular-motor control (Nobak & Demarest, 1975). Pathological development is evaluated by significant early deviations in the occurrence of primitive reflexes, postural reflexes, and related vestibular processes.

Neurological reflexes are involuntary motor responses that are elicited by specific peripheral stimuli. Major developmental theorists have recognized the early reflex patterns as important for later development (Gesell, 1940; Piaget, 1971; Watson, 1962). A broad range of reflexes occurs in early infancy only to later disappear and the significance of many of these reflexes for later development is not known. However, the persistence of some of these reflexes beyond the first year of life can be significant. For example, the Palmer grasp (Twitchell, 1965) and the Moro reflexes (Mitchell, l960) can be elicited during the first 6-12 months of life, and in the normal course of development, can no longer be elicited except in certain cases of cerebral insult. The persistence of these reflexes in the infant beyond the first year has been considered a sign of CNS dysfunction for over fifty years (Sanford, 1933). Body postural reflexes contribute to maintain the characteristic orientation of the body in space with respect to gravity. The vestibular apparatus plays an important role in posture through the vestibular-ocular-motor pathways and the vestibular-spinal tracts (Magnus, 1926). A closely related function of the postural reflexes is the maintenance of the interrelationship of body parts. During the first year of life, this interrelationship is maintained at a reflex level by such reflexes as neck righting, and is later maintained by more voluntary coordinated responses, such as segmental rolling (Milani-Comparetti & Gidoni, 1967).

Developmental Sequence

Abnormalities in the early development of particular reflexes and equilibrium reactions have pathological implications in themselves (Capute et al., 1978). However, it is the developmental interrelationship between these reflexes and reactions that has particular significance in terms of early pathology and the failure in the child's ability to learn. The acquisition of visually guided prehension is a major milestone in cognitive development (Piaget, 1952) and the close relationship between the evolution of the grasp reflex in the hand and its significance in the developmental stages of prehension has been established (Twitchell, 1965). Abnormalities in the early modification of primitive reflexes and the development of a broad range of coordinated motor behaviors appear to be causal factors in the learning problems of a variety of children.

This observation is based on the clinically established link between reflex and gross-motor milestones observed primarily in infants (Capute et al., 1978; Milani-Comparetti & Gidoni, 1967). During the first year or so of life there are a number of reflexes that are relatively easy to elicit. In the normal course of events, these reflexes gradually become inhibited or more difficult to elicit. This occurs during the first year and reflects the maturation of the CNS. This orderly suppression of reflexes is associated with successive stages of motor accomplishments that generally reflect the development of equilibrium and the child's adaptation to gravity. The development of equilibrium necessary for standing and walking is based on the earlier development of a cluster of reflexes not apparent at birth, referred to as postural adjustment reflexes. These reflexes appear gradually during the first year, and when fully mature function as automatic reactions. The inhibition of the primitive reflexes and the integrated function of postural reflexes, such as body righting, are closely related to the acquisition of major motor milestones. These milestones are indicators of the child's adaptation to gravity as seen in rolling, sitting, creeping, standing and finally walking. This intricate interplay between gravity and equilibrium is normally concluded during the first 12-16 months of life. To simplify what is essentially a complex

13

process occurring in a relatively brief period of time, two simultaneously proceeding processes that are related temporally must occur: adaptive inhibition of primitive reflexes and development of postural reflexes. The abnormal development of this sequence has been clinically investigated in two groups of children having CNS pathology: the mentally retarded and the cerebral palsied.

Mental Retardation

Although the use of level of intelligence as a means of diagnosing and classifying the mentally retarded has its own shortcomings, its long and continued use suggests that it has clinical as well as research value. However, because the evaluation of intelligence in infancy and early childhood is a difficult technical task, especially with the atypical infant, and because of the low correlation between early and later intelligence, the diagnostic value of an intellectual evaluation for mental retardation in this age range is limited. The more severe the mental retardation, the less this is so (Morrison, Pothier & Horr, 1978). Delay in intellectual development is frequently associated with delays in motor development in this population, and there are indications that the assessment of motor milestones may be a useful diagnostic procedure for the early detection of mental retardation. For example, there appears to be a relationship between intellectual level and motor milestones, such as sitting and walking. Children with moderate retardation tend to accomplish sitting and walking at a later time than do children functioning in the mildly retarded range (Illingworth, 1968). A number of researchers have established the significance of delays in motor development as a sensitive indicator of not only the occurrence but severity of mental retardation (Donoghue et al., 1970). Early signs, useful in predicting the degree of later mental retardation, are significant delays in both walking and use of language (Neligan & Prudham, 1969).

Although there is evidence of an association between delays in motor development and mental retardation, the details of this relationship are not well known. Clinical data suggests that irregularities in the inhibition of primitive reflexes and development of postural adjustments may contribute to the delays in motor development in the mentally retarded (Morrison et al., 1978). A series of clinical studies has established that the absence or presence of the placing reaction is related to severity of mental retardation. Children with severe

14

retardation characteristically failed to demonstrate this reflex in all four limbs while children in the moderate and mild retarded were negative for this sign (Zapella, Foley & Cookson, 1964). There is some evidence that abnormalities in the development of postural reflexes may play a more important role in the delay of motor development than the lack of inhibition in primitive reflexes. In a prospective study of 53 retarded infants and young children without evidence of a frank physical disability, Molnar (1978) found that delayed motor development was related to the delay in the appearance of postural adjustment reactions rather than the persistence of reflex patterns. Primitive reflexes, such as the asymmetrical tonic neck, appeared to be inhibited normally, whereas propping and equilibrium responses were delayed. Postural adjustment tended to appear prior to the appearance of motor milestones, but both developed significantly later than normally expected.

The difficulty in evaluating all of these studies is the absence of more quantitative measurements of either the primitive reflexes or postural adjustments. More sensitive measurement techniques may show more subtle relationships that would fail to be established using a clinical evaluation of present or absent. Postural adjustments must not just occur but must be adequate to maintain equilibrium. This is a matter of degree rather than occurrence or non-occurrence. There is evidence that by applying more sensitive evaluation techniques, the tonic neck reflex can be elicited in normal children of school age (Parmenter, 1975). Had such a technique been used on the Molnar (1978) research, it is possible that a relationship between inadequate inhibition of such reflexes and delayed development of postural adjustments would have been demonstrated.

Cerebral Palsy

The early diagnosis of cerebral palsy is a crucial step in formulating an effective treatment program. Although the assumption is made that this non-progressive disorder in posture and motion is due to CNS injury, the actual diagnosis is difficult to make during the first year of life. In cases of clearly documented trauma and gross abnormalities in equilibrium and motor development, the diagnostic issues are less complex, but where the history is less clear or the diagnostic signs less reliable, such as in cases of minimal cerebral palsy (Wigglesworth, 1961), diagnostic issues occur. Clinical research has indicated that abnormalities in the inhibition of primitive reflexes and the development of postural responses during the first year or so of life, may be the most sensitive early indicators of cerebral palsy (Bobath & Bobath, 1975). Clinical research has focused on a host of reflexes including the Moro, tonic neck, Landau, and righting reactions (Capute et al., 1978; Milani-Comparetti & Gidoni, 1965). For example, Paine (1964) periodically examined a group of infants considered at risk for CNS pathology beginning at six months and continuing until 36 months. Clinical evaluations of primitive reflexes, postural adjustments and developmental milestones during this interval, established that only deviations in the asymmetrical tonic neck reflex related to motor development.

One of the difficulties in evaluating the data in this area, as in the clinical research with the mentally retarded, has been the lack of quantitative scales for assessment purposes. Clinical researchers have used simple occurrence or non-occurrence criterion, or subjective judgements of gradation of severity, that make replication difficult. In response to this problem, efforts have been made to develop evaluation scales that have the quantitative characteristic necessary for the establishment of reliability and validity (Capute et al., 1978). Such scales should move the evaluation process beyond dichotomous assessment and provide important longitudinal data on the possible interrelationship between lack of inhibition of primitive reflexes and the development of postural reflexes and equilibrium reactions. A particular group of reflexes appears to be significant in terms of the early evaluation of cerebral palsy. These include reactions to maintain erect posture, segmental rolling, and the Galant, Moro, and tonic neck reflexes. Efforts have been made to quantify the occurrence of these signs for the evaluation of cerebral palsy (Capute et al., 1978) and a similar effort has been made to establish a quantified evaluation of some of the same signs in the learning disabled population (Ayres, 1980; Pothier, Friedlander, Morrison & Herman, 1983).

Although efforts to quantify the evaluation of these reflexes in the cerebral palsied population are recent, the clinical literature in this area extends back approximately thirty years (Bobath & Bobath, 1956). Considering the importance of motor development in early childhood learning and in the acquisition of learning in general, the clinical observations of the cerebral palsied child and of how the persistence of primitive reflexes can inhibit other areas of development are pertinent to the understanding of how these reflexes may interfere with learning acquisition in the LD population. At its simplest

16

descriptive level, the asymmetrical tonic neck reflex essentially affects the muscle tone in the arms and legs with extension occurring on the face side and flexion occurring on the skull side when the head is turned. The effects of the failure of this reflex to be inhibited after the first year of life has been clinically observed in children with cerebral palsy (Bobath & Bobath, 1975). If the reflex is strong, it interferes with the child using both hands together for grasp support when sitting or standing, and the asymmetrical distribution of muscle tone throughout the body makes maintenance of balance in any position difficult and sometimes impossible. This effect is observed in the cerebral palsied child who walks with the head averted to one side using extensor hypertonus of the leg on the face side for weight-bearing. This results in the opposite leg being used to step forward while the extensor leg follows. Any situation that requries hand-head-eye coordination, such as the simple act of eating, will be difficult. When the elbow is flexed, the head tends to turn away from that arm, and consequently, away from the food the flexed limb is bringing toward the head. These conditions observed in the more severe cases of CNS pathology, such as cerebral palsy, serve as prototypes of behaviors observed frequently in LD children. In these children, the elicitation of the tonic neck reflex in situations requiring hand-head-eye coordination, may not be as observable during eating, but may be observed in the kindergarten-aged child who is having difficulty in drawing a straight line from left to right. At a mechanical level, the need to turn the head to guide the pencil results in an increase in extensor tone in the right-handed child or flexor tone in the left-handed child. In either case the inadequately inhibited reflex interferes with the hand-head-eye coordination necessary to accomplish a task that is basic to learning how to write.

Conclusion

The clinical data suggesting a relationship between inadequate inhibition of primitive reflexes and the deviant development of postural adjustments, and the more complex equilibrium reactions needed for walking, is impressive. However, at this point, the data indicates an association rather than a functional relationship. This situation could be changed, perhaps, with the development of more quantitative scales for evaluation. The issue here for medical research is similar to a prevailing one in the behavioral sciences: reliability and validity of behavioral measurements. Moving into this area of research with the learning disabled, the methodological issues are similar. However, considerable efforts have been made to objectify and quantify the assessment procedures used with the learning disabled child. Rather than assessing the preschool aged child, which has been typical of the research in pediatrics with the mentally retarded and cerebral palsied child, the focus here has been with the identified LD population: the school-aged child from age 6 to 12. The efforts at quantification are respectable and certainly adequate for research and clinical purposes.

These efforts have moved this research more into the arena of behavioral science with its characteristic focus on quantification and operational definitions of observable behavior. To varying degrees, there has been less of a focus on the unmeasureable but hypothesized neuropathology. Research with the LD population has suggested added involvement of the vestibular system. Consequently, there has been more effort to measure vestibular processing dysfunctions, such as equilibrium reactions, nystagmus and ocular-motor control. As an added dimension of this research, systematic investigation of related perceptual processing functions, such as visual tracking, sequencing and bilateral integration has been prevalent.

The empirical basis for the contribution of neurobehavioral dysfunction to childhood pathology in general, and learning disability specifically, has evolved primarily from medical research and practice. Consequently, much of the theoretical basis for conceptualizing and understanding the relationship between neurobehavioral dysfunction and learning disabilities has been more influenced by the methods and data of neurophysical research rather than behavioral science. This has resulted in an unbalanced theoretical view of the field that may be mitigated by the contribution of a more behavioral approach to learning acquisition and learning disorders.

Chapter 3

Neurobehavioral Factors in Learning Acquisition in Childhood: Theoretical Basis

Introduction

The theoretical basis for assessing neurobehavioral integration in learning disabled children is directly related to various assumptions regarding the role played by these functions in normal learning. Since the child, a developing organism, is of concern, the unique contribution of neurobehavioral functions to learning acquisition is a major focus. This is an important theoretical consideration. NBD in a LD child can account for the child's current state in terms of etiology, but can also suggest various intervention strategies that may influence the acquisition of learning skills. Both assumptions regarding etiology and future learning acquisition are based on three major assertions. Certainly a major premise is that information from the senses and perception interact and significantly contribute to learning acquisition. This premise is shared with other approaches to learning disabilities, such as that exemplified by neuropsychology, and is not particularly unique to the neurobehavioral approach. Unique to neurobehavioral theory is the assertion of the significant contribution of the proprioceptive system and motor action to the learning process. In fact, motoric action on the environment and consequent feedback is a major organizing factor in the child's perception of sensory experience. As expressed by Ayres (1961): "Purposeful movement is the *sine qua non* in the development of body scheme, for it provides the opportunity to synthesize and derive meaning about the body from many sources of information, especially vision, touch and proprioception" (p. 99).

The importance of motoric action in organizing perception and the contribution of perception to learning are two major theoretical assumptions. Any factor that would interfere with the normal integrating functions of action and/or perception could potentially result in significant variations in learning acquisition. Various factors might contribute to this process, but the factors that have received the most attention from those interested in neurobehavioral dysfunctions are related to the vestibular system: "...we must reason that, as intentional and coordinated motor activity allows the presence of learning processes, postural systems permit the development of motor activity" (deQuiros & Schrager, 1979, p. 30).

These assumptions regarding learning, perception and action are consistently linked to a particular form of treatment whenever there is evidence that NBD exists. According to deQuiros and Schrager, (1979), "... one fact remains: motor activity is essential in order to learn. In pathological cases (for instance, the cerebral palsies) the therapist must stabilize the body and rule its movements in order to obtain real learning" (p. 25).

The three major assertions regarding learning acquisition are (1) perception is an organizer of sensory information and basic to all learning, (2) movement and contingent environmental feedback are major factors in integrated perception, and (3) the major neurobehavioral system contributing to movement, perception and learning is the vestibular-proprioceptive. In developmental sequence this type of learning appears first and must be adequately integrated before more cognitive-type learning processes, such as reading, can develop normally. Frequently, this sequence is also conceptualized neurologically, with brain stem and sub-cortical functions making major contributions to the earliest learning acquisition, while the neocortex plays a major role in later cognitive growth. "As long as subcortical structures remain poorly integrated, resolution of the impairment through a cognitive approach will be limited, for neocortical processing is dependent upon subcortical processes for optimum function" (Ayres, 1972a, p. 52).

This emphasis on sequence, and the different type of learning that is acquired from one sequence to another, is not unique to neurobehavioral theory. However, the conception of subcortical neurological functions operating as independent variables, with learning as the dependent variable, and the need to link a theory of learning to a theory and practice of therapy, is unique. This has resulted in some major criticism of the theory, in which the difficulties in demonstrating the effectiveness of the therapy has been a causal factor in rejecting the assertions regarding learning. Moreover, the persistence in relating particular types of neurobehavioral dysfunctions to specific

20

types of therapeutic intervention has resulted in criticism regarding the equivocal status of the signs of these dysfunctions and their contribution to learning disabilities.

Examination of the relevant literature indicates that two individuals, Ayres (1972a) and deQuiros (1976), have been particularly influential in contributing to the theoretical thinking in this field. In order to evaluate the theory appropriately, it will be important to examine the research and theory that has influenced these theorists. For an adequate criticism, particular attention must be given to the relationship of the vestibular-proprioceptive system to perception, the organizing function of motoric-action and environmental feedback for perception, and the contribution of all these factors to the learning process.

Vestibular-Proprioceptive System

Neurobehavioral dysfunction does not appear to be acquired after birth, and the dysfunctions are found in the reflex systems and interrelated vestibular proprioceptive systems of the LD child. The fact that these children also demonstrate learning disabilities stimulates interest, as well as attempts, in linking the cognitive problems with the dysfunctional vestibular proprioceptive system. Logically, although perhaps difficult to do, attempts should be made to find children demonstrating vestibular-proprioceptive dysfunctions and not having learning disabilties. There is an assumed causal relationship and this can only be investigated by having the independent variable, in this case the dysfunctional system, manipulated along some dimension, while the dependent variable, the learning disability, is examined. Obviously, because of various considerations, this would have to be a quasi-experimental design.

The general evidence for the role played by the vestibular-proprioceptive system in learning is considerable. Research on the development of the nervous system indicates that the vestibular pathways are the first to mylenate and that this may be due to the effect of gravitational forces on the vestibular organs of the fetus between the fifth and sixth month of pregnancy. Although there is evidence that cerebellar and reticular functions influence posture and motion, research has established the major contributions of the vestibular system in the complex interrelated development of primitive reflexes, postural adjustments, equilibrium reactions, and ocular-motor control (Ayres,

21

1972a, Chap. 5; deQuiros & Schrager, 1978, Chaps. 2 & 5; Kornhuber, 1974). Although a great deal of the data is based on research with animals, the vestibular system contributes to posture chiefly through the vestibular—ocular motor pathways, controlling eye movements, and through the vestibular-spinal tracts to control equilibrium. In terms of learning, ocular-motor control is clearly basic for visual-motor coordination and the perceptual-motor process necessary for writing or reading (Leisman & Schwartz, 1976). At an even more basic level, posture and equilibrium are important for movement and motoric action, and movement and motoric action are organizers of perception.

Motor Activity and Learning

A number of learning theorists and developmental psychologists have emphasized the importance of the response-side of learning acquisition. Response and contingent reinforcement have been central to both drive reduction and reinforcement theory (Marx, 1951). At a more cognitive level, sensorimotor intelligence, which is characteristic of intelligence during the first two years of life, develops because of the interaction of the circular reactions and systematic feedback from the environment (Piaget, 1954). These circular reactions evolve from a reflex base and are important for the development of both pre-operational and operational thought. Neurobehavioral theorists emphasize two major interrelated aspects of motoric actions: its importance for sensory integration and its contributions to the development of body image (Ayres, 1961, 1972a, pp. 28-31; deQuiros & Schrager, 1979, pp. 24-29).

There are a number of studies indicating that a frequently found problem in LD children is inadequate intermodal sensory association (Lerner, 1981, pp. 206-217). This dysfunction in sensory integration is basic to the perceptual processing and learning disorders observed in these children. The development of sensory integration and learning is greatly influenced by purposeful motoric action which engages the various sense modalities simultaneously. Research on the effects of early deprivation and learning, and studies of the effects of "enriched" environments on learning, all done with animals as subjects, are presented as support for this point of view. Motoric factors as determinants in perception have received substantial research and theoretical support (Held, 1973; Werner & Wapner, 1949). A frequently cited reference in the literature on neurobehavioral dysfunction is the research of Held (1973). Wearing prisms that distorted their visual perception, subjects experienced an unfamiliar perceptual task by either being moved passively through it or by walking actively through it. In either situation the actual visual input would be the same. Subjects who were active demonstrated greater adaptation to the prisms than did the passive subjects.

Sensory integration and adequate perception, once established, become automatic functions. For example, the vestibular-proprioceptive system is constantly providing information to the child regarding equilibrium, motion, and space. In the normal course of events this information, although constantly contributing to adaptation and body scheme, is no longer a focus of consciousness, although it can be. With the learning disabled child, constant conscious efforts must be made to use the information and the information itself is inadequate because of a basic dysfunction in sensory integration.

Neurobehavioral Dysfunction as a Cause of Learning Disability

At one level it is meaningful to state that learning disabilities develop because of problems in sensory integration and consequent perceptual processing problems. However, this is a very general statement and theoretical clarity would be advanced if a more precise statement could be made. The assertion is broad enough to account for a great deal, yet too broad to be useful in the details of what it does and does not account for. There has been some attempt to sharpen the theoretical utility of some of the assertions. Ayres' attempts (1972a, Chap. 1) are closely tied to neurology and the need to develop a rationale for a particular form of therapy. Referring to the theory of Lassek (1957), Ayres assumes that the brain's evolution and capacity for cognitive thought evolved because of prolonged environmental stress acting on an organisum with an urge to respond and the capacity to change. The major evolutionary change was the neurological development of sensory systems that increased the human organism's perceptual capacities. These latter capacities developed from the even more basic mechanoreceptors related to touch, gravity, and movement. The forces that influence the phyletic development of the human brain assume a role in ontogenetic development. The environment impinges on a normally sensitive child with a growing nervous system

23

and, as a consequence of that stress, the brain develops. Learning disabilities develop in a child whose nervous system cannot respond to environmental stress. In evolution, the human capacity to do this resulted in the development of the senses and finally cognition and intelligence. In the individual child with an inadequate capacity to integrate sensation and perception, the later developing cognitive capacities will not evolve.

Another function of the brain that receives major emphasis by Ayres is the plasticity of neural function. This is more characteristic of the younger, rather than older, human organism, and is based on the effect of motor activity on skeletal development and sensory-motor activity on neural growth. Although neurological organization is assumed to be completed by the first decade of life, recent research indicates that in the young organism neurological damage and dysfunction can be compensated by the capacity of the brain to reorganize and regain functions. This capacity is greatly stimulated by appropriate environmental stress. The logical step from this data to a theory of therapy is made: "Plasticity of neural function is one of the qualities upon which man's phylogeny, his ontogeny, and the success of an intervention program directed toward ameliorating sensory integrative dysfunction, are dependent" (Ayres, 1972a, p. 16).

Probably the clearest example of Ayres' consistent tendency to relate neurological theory to learning disabilities, and therapy, is seen in the following: "It is not unreasonable to suppose that dendritic growth in influenced by early environment; thus the greater the use made of neuronal synapses, the greater the aborization of dendrites, with resultant greater learning capacity of the organism. That something of this nature might happen during sensory integrative therapy with the young child should not be overlooked" (Ayres, 1972a, p. 18).

The attempt by Ayres to establish a more concise theoretical relationship between neurobehavioral functions and learning is characterized by a great deal of speculation regarding the nervous system, particularly the brain. Explanatory emphasis is on neurological functions as they affect perception and cognition. Much less attention is given to the interaction effects of these three factors. Environmental manipulations, particularly sensory integration therapy, are effective because they probably change the actual neurophysiological processes. It is then the change at this neurological level that in some unspecified way results in major modifications in perceptual-cognitive processes. The result of this focus is that a therapist using this technique is never simply modifying behavior. If behavior is modified this is a result of an assumed, but vaguely conceptualized, physiological change in the brain. The logical problem with this approach is that the only measurement of change, or lack of change, is behavior. The independent variables are unmeasured subcortical functions:

> While academic and other learning certainly involves portions of the cerebral cortex, those portions are not only interdependent but dependent upon lower neural structures for normal functioning. For that reason remedial intervention programs must first be concerned with brain function, especially the older and lower parts. These functions are carried out through brain mechanisms (Ayres, 1972a, p. 23).

The explanatory utility of referring to unknown, because at this point unmeasurable, neurological variables is limited. One of these limitations is that the vagueness of the assertions and operational definitions result in the theory being difficult to test. deQuiros (1976) and deQuiros and Schrager (1979) have used a similar developmental view as that utilized by Ayres, but have attempted to relate neurobehavioral functions more directly to cognitive development, particularly consciousness.

Again, vestibular and proprioceptive functions have a major influence on sensory integration and perceptual development. In addition, since young children have not yet established cerebral dominance, any early dysfunctions in the vestibular proprioceptive system will affect the development of cerebral dominance. As body information is integrated and spatial relationships established, automatic purposeful motor acts are generally relegated to the right hemisphere while communication skills are a function of the left hemisphere. However, in cases of neurobehavioral dysfunction, stable body schemes and perceptual functions do not develop and consequently hemispheric lateralization is often disrupted. This has important cognitive consequences. In the development sequence, the emergence of cerebral dominance is associated with automatic control of posture, equilibrium, and purposeful motor acts. In cases of neurobehavioral dysfunction, these processes require voluntary control through conscious effort. This results in a hierarchy in consciousness in which body-spatial information dominates and symbolic conceptual systems do not receive adequate conscious attention.

As is typical of the theoretical efforts in this area, there is a need to reduce this to some rather vague neurological constructs:

> When the circuits available to handle corporal-spatial information are inadequate, circuits which should be used for higher programs are called

into action. Higher level circuits then become overloaded with body information while correcting for lower circuit inadequacies. Thus higher circuits are not free to fulfill their appropriate functions (deQuiros, 1976, p. 52).

Although it is clear that the above is presented as a meaningful contribution and clarification of theory, it is also clear that this is a limited metaphor to explain what must be a complex neurophysiological process that needs to be given the conceptual status of a hypothetical construct (Marx, 1951). At a more behavioral level, the assertion does have the implication that a child must be able to exclude data from the neurobehavioral functions from awareness, particularly the vestibular, in order to attend to the learning of language, speech, reading, writing and other symbolic processes related to communication. These later developing cognitive capacities will be related in turn to hemispheric specialization that will also be delayed or disrupted in the child with NBD. All these latter assertions are testable and therefore have the potential to add empirical support to the theory.

These ideas regarding conscious awareness and learning were later elaborated upon with the concept of corporal potentiality (deQuiros & Schrager, 1979, Chap. 2). The body is continuously giving the individual information about its current state such as temperature, pain, and posture. At times consciousness can be directed to this information, but in general, in order for symbolic learning to take place, such bodily information should be inhibited or excluded from consciousness. The development of language is influenced through motoric-action, as suggested in Piaget's theory, but to think with language requires more than purposeful equilibrium and motoric-action. To think symbolically requires noninterference at a conscious level of bodily sensations. This is referred to as corporal potentiality and this capacity must be functioning adequately before later developing cognitive systems evolve. Developmentally, purposeful equilibrium and motion will be a focus of awareness and contribute to learning acquisition during the earlier periods of childhood. Later in childhood, much of this data will be automatic and inhibited from awareness because of corporal potentiality. Consequently, the more symbolic operations of thought become the subject of conscious awareness.

26

Criticism

The preceding review of theory has emphasized neurobehavioral factors as they relate to normal learning and learning disabilities. Ayres, deQuiros and Schrager are aware that learning disabilities may develop from perceptual processes not directly related to vestibular-proprioceptive functions and that such disabilities may also develop from causes other than neurobehavioral dysfunctions. However, their major focus, theoretical as well as research, has been on vestibular-proprioceptive variables. Major criticisms have been made of theories that stress perceptual-motor factors in learning and learning disabilities (Mann, 1970; Velluntino, Steger, Mayer, Harding & Niles, 1977). These critiques have consistently confounded the empirical and theoretical basis of the approach with the effectiveness of perceptual-motor therapy and sensory integration therapy. In what follows, the effectiveness of the therapy will receive no comment. The existence of perceptual processing problems and neurobehavioral dysfunctions and their relationship to learning disabilities is an empirical issue. The theoretical efforts to establish their relationship to learning and learning disabilities can be evaluated independently of any results of a particular type of therapy.

Brain and Behavior

The issues in adequately assessing brain dysfunction and then describing the behavior that is the result of such dysfunction have received considerable attention (Ross, 1973; Rutter, 1982). As should be clear from the previous presentation of Ayres and deQuiros, there is a tendency to explain behavior by reference to underlying neurological functions. The brain becomes the independent variable and behavior the dependent variable. The conceptual issues in this approach are significant and numerous and a few of them will be addressed here.

The strongest support for relating behavior to brain abnormalities comes from cases where normal behavior was known to occur and then change significantly with the occurrence of demonstrable CNS disease or trauma (Hynd & Obrzut, 1981, Chap 1). Much of the evidence for this relationship between brain and behavior comes from studies of adults rather than children. As has been previously noted, the population of children of interest in this text are those who have no history of CNS disease or trauma yet demonstrate vestibular dysfunctions, perceptual processing problems and learning disabilities. With this population, the continuum model of brain dysfunction has been used. In these cases a subclinical brain damage occurs that is not diagnosed by the usual neurological exam and is accompanied by a set pattern of behaviors. There is evidence that there is such a population, but that (1) the early brain injuries had to be severe for a behavioral sequelae to occur, (2) the behavior cannot be described as homogeneous, and (3) such minimal brain dysfunctions (MBD) are probably relatively uncommon (Rutter, 1982).

Examination of the literature in this area indicates that a disease model is being used to explain behavior. In known cases of brain trauma or disease, behavioral changes in perception and cognition occur and are symptomatic of the neuropathology. By analogy, the dysfunction in perception and cognition observed in the learning disabled child is a symptom of some underlying neural pathology. One of the major logical difficulties in using this approach is that the measures of behavior, although less than perfect, are more reliable and valid than the direct measures of the underlying neuropathology. In fact, in the case of MBD, the only measure of neuropathology is behavioral. Once the observer moves beyond describing the relationship between measurable stimulus events and behavior by drawing inferences regarding mediating processes, he is using hypothetical constructs. In terms of neurobehavioral functions, Ayres and deQuiros consistently move from describing functional relationships between neurobehavioral measures, such as nystagmus duration and performance on a perceptual task, to a statement regarding the underlying neurological structure. Sensory integration can only be assessed by behavioral functions and it is beyond our current store of knowledge regarding neurophysiology to state clearly how sensory integration is a function of cortical and subcortical structures. At times, the theoretical concepts are more at the level of metaphor rather than hypothetical constructs (Ayres, 1972a, p. 11; deQuiros, 1976, p. 52).

The Sensory and Perceptual Basis of Learning

A major assumption in this approach is that there is a hierarchy in learning: sensory and perceptual functions become integrated through action, and early integration at this level is basic for adequate cognitive learning. This assumption regarding sequence and hierarchy is frequently related to cortical and subcortical functions and the use of certain therapeutic modalities. Support for this assertion is obtained by references to the theories of Piaget (Ayres, 1972a, p. 5; deQuiros & Schrager, pp. 24, 233) and Werner and Wapner (Ayres, 1972a, p. 15) and by reference to studies providing evidence that motoric responses and sensory and perceptual variables contribute to cognitive learning. However, the implication that the development is sequential ignores the evidence that it is interactive, and the stress on the response side of learning ignores the evidence that a significant amount of learning is observational (Bandura, 1969).

The importance of the circular reactions during the first two years of life for the development of sensorimotor intelligence in Piaget's theory is clear (Piaget, 1954). However, even during this period of time the child is demonstrating the cognitive capacity for immediate and delayed imitation that is not a direct function of motoric action. An examination of the theory also indicates that it is the interaction between perception and operational thought that characterizes the child's earliest schemas with the more stable operational systems increasingly directing the child's thinking. That this is the case, not only in terms of theory but in terms of empirical data, is supported by a considerable amount of research (Wachs, 1976).

The research and theory of Werner and Wapner (1949) strongly support the view that human perception cannot be adequately explained by variables such as sensory qualities, dimensions, surface, contour and figure. Research stimulated by the sensory-tonic field theory is interpreted by these theorists as indicating that perception was a function of proprioceptive variables such as muscle tension and movements. A direct elaboration of this theory was later used to account for personality development along the dimensions of differentiated and undifferentiated (Witkins et al., 1962). The sensory-tonic theory of perception and the field dependent-independent personality type were empirically based on research. However, the central problem for the sensory-tonic field theory, and for the theoretical efforts of Ayres and deQuiros, is to account for how exteroceptive variables, such as visual-perception in the rod and frame experiment, interact with proprioceptive variables, such as the muscle tension generated by body tilt, to influence veridical or non-veridical judgment. In a detailed analysis of the research and theory, Allport (1955, Chap. 8) concluded that is was, theoretically speaking, gratuitous to maintain that there were two separate variables, one sensory and the other tonic, that produced the effect in perception. The meaning of the sensory variables has never been adequately differentiated from that of the tonic variables, and the use of the postulate of a sensory-tonic energy exchange to account for differences between the two does not contribute substantially to solving the conceptual problem.

Neurobehavioral Syndromes

References to directly unobservable processes, such as subcortical functions, to explain behavior phenomena at a theoretical level, will have limited value until either a direct measure of the process is made available or a useful behavioral measure is obtained. Neurobehavioral syndromes are in some ways like hypothetical constructs. Like a hypothetical construct, there is more to a syndrome than the various. methods used to measure it. However, without a sufficient system of measurement, a syndrome does not exist, just as finally a useful hypothetical construct does not exist unless there is a supporting network of operations to define it. The first step in establishing the existence of a syndrome is to adequately measure the various signs of it. These signs of neurobehavioral functions can be defined and operationalized by directly observable behaviors such as the tonic neck reflexes and ocular–motor control. The behavioral theorist and scientist must be conscious of the need for adequate operational definitions. The clinician, who may also be a theorist or scientist, should be equally conscious of the value of establishing operational definitions, that is, reliable and valid behavioral measures of the deviant behavior patterns to be assessed.

Although Ayres (1972a, Chap. 7) and deQuiros and Schrager (1978, Chap. 10) have been interested in establishing syndromes based on observed behavior, an examination of their efforts indicates that there has not been adequate attention given to establishing reliable procedures to measure behavior. For example, the inter-scorer reliability of the various scales used to establish the syndromes described by Ayres (1972a) are not reported or are not known (Ayres, 1980). The use of factor analytic procedures to establish syndromes that are based on behavioral measures of unreported reliability would result in failure of replication. The existence of two different syndromes, vestibular-proprioceptive dissociation and vestibular-ocular-motor-split, have been discussed by deQuiros and Schrager (1979, pp. 189-194). This effort is probably the best example of the tendency to mix neurophysiological assumptions with poorly defined behavioral

30

categories. The issues and problems in establishing measures of behavior that can be useful both clinically and scientifically have not been adequately dealt with. Neurobehavioral syndromes like intelligence can only be defined by measurable behavior at this time, and like the measurement of intelligence, this requires considerable time and psychometric sophistication. Contemporary examples of the procedures used in developing a scientifically respectable and clinically useful intelligence test suggest a model that might be followed to establish neurobehavioral syndromes (Kaufman & Kaufman, 1983; Wechsler, 1974).

Conclusion

The development of and support for a useful theory can come from various sources, but a behavioral theory must be supported by operational definitions and behavioral data. The position taken in this text is that a neglected area in neurobehavioral theory, research, assessment, and intervention has been the establishment of scientifically sound and clinically useful behavioral assessment procedures. In terms of theory development, these measures would be the operational definitions and would be the first step in establishing intervening constructs. In terms of the establishment of syndromes, the first step would be in establishing the reliability and validity of the various signs that form the syndrome. At this point in time there is concern as to whether or not these signs should be considered as having equivocal or nonequivocal status as indicators of pathology (Rutter, 1982). In what follows, an effort will be made to establish the status of these signs in terms of reliability, degree of validity, and relationship to perceptual processing problems and learning disabilities in children. A working assumption that some learning disabilities, such as reading retardation, are due to perceptual processing problems that are part of a general neurobehavioral dysfunction, will be used throughout the presentation and discussion of the data. The following review will indicate that the signs of neurobehavioral dysfunction should be considered as having unequivocal status and that there is significant empirical support for the working assumption.

Chapter 4

Neurobehavioral Dysfunction: Research

Introduction

One of the values of theory is that it stimulates research. Frequently the goal of this research will be to obtain data that either provides support for the theory or provides clearer statements regarding what the theory does account for or what it cannot explain. In this regard, a useful theory should have some postulates that can be tested. For example, the construct of corporal potentiality (deQuiros, 1976) has characteristics that can be operationalized and perhaps put to some test that would support or not support the construct. Another way of evaluating the usefulness of a theory of learning disabilities is to view it in terms of the context of discovery and the context of confirmation (Marx, 1951).

In the initial stage of the development of scientific ideas, wherein hypotheses are generated, the methods of discovery vary considerably. Dependent on multiple uncontrolled and probably uncontrollable factors, ideas may be generated by private, subjective, intuitive, creative and accidental ways in which an individual thinks. At this point there are no generally agreed upon standards for evaluating or monitoring the process. The ideas generated during this initial process must be formulated in such a way as to be testable in order for the theory to attract scientific interest. Scientific methods will then be applied in the crucial test of systematically evaluating the hypothesis through observation. The minimal condition for scientific usefulness is that an idea has consequences that can be tested. This is the context of confirmation.

Many ideas regarding learning and learning disabilities have been generated by clinical observations. From these observations a host of clinical interpretations are made that serve to discriminate between observations and to generalize among observations, for example, the component behaviors that are part of a syndrome of vestibular processing dysfunction that distinguish it from some other syndrome. Further removed from observation, clinical interpretation, discrimination and generalization, is theory. At the point of theory, concepts which are implicit in the interpretation of the behavior observed or to which interpretations may lead, such as corporal potentiality, play a more active and organizing role. Theory, at this level, becomes useful as an organizer of data by providing more general concepts that to some degree explain the data. Theories, such as those of Ayres and deQuiros and Schrager, may be evaluated at any level, but at this time it would seem that the most useful evaluation would be at the level of the context of confirmation of the clinical observations on which the theory is based.

Clinical Observation and Scientific Method

The more consistently the consequences of an idea generated from clinical observation are confirmed, the more confidence one has in the idea. Somewhat like psychoanalytic theory (Achenbach & Lewis, 1971), the confirmation of neurobehavioral theory has been addressed in the context of therapy outcome as well as the assessment of behavior and establishment of syndromes. In some ways this is unfortunate because logically the usefulness of the theory is not entirely dependent on a set of intervention techniques. Some of this has been generated by the positions taken by the theorists themselves, who consistently relate assessment to therapeutic intervention. As was noted earlier, the clinical observation that NBD and perceptual processing problems are the cause of cognitive learning disabilities has been criticized (Mann, 1970; Velluntino et al., 1977) and the effectiveness of sensory integration therapy and/or perceptual motor training for learning disabilities has not received consistent research support (Kavale & Mattson, 1983). A review of the relevant literature relating to NBD indicates that a great deal of the difficulties in the context of confirmation may be due to inadequate research method and design in the study of both assessment and intervention. An examination of the most recent negative evaluation of research in perceptual motor training and assessment (Kavale & Mattson, 1983) indicates that although sensory integration assessment and therapy are included in the evaluation, only one study using procedures identified with this approach is mentioned (Ayres, 1972b). The major focus is on perceptual-motor training as developed by such clinicians as Frostig (1970) and Kephart (1960). Procedures developed in the area of NBD are similar to those found in perceptual-motor training but also differ in meaningful ways.

The following critique relates directly to the research on assessment and intervention primarily concerned with NBD within the vestibular-proprioceptive system. Particular methodological and design problems have resulted in difficulties interpreting the results of this research. The interrelated problems to be discussed are: (1) Subject Selection and Description, (2) Sampling, (3) Treatment Comparisons, (4) Independent Variables and Dependent Variables, and (5) Analysis of data. Following the discussion of these issues as they relate to research in NBD in general, a more detailed analysis of one study related to assessment and another study on intervention will be presented.

Subject Selection

It is generally agreed that within the group of children assessed as being learning disabled there is considerable heterogeneity in terms of type of learning disability, as well as variables such as social-economic class, degree of behavioral disturbance, attention-concentration and hyperactivity (Lerner, 1981, Chap. 1). In any study in which learning disabled children are subjects, explicit statements regarding inclusion and exclusion criteria must be made. Each decision regarding the variables to be allowed in or excluded out of the sample must be based on some sort of measurement. The less reliable, or more variable the measurement, the more variability will be found within and between subjects. This will affect outcome and efforts at replication in studies of assessment and/or intervention. However, it becomes an added problem in terms of intervention research. Inclusion or exclusion criteria involves variables, for example hyperactivity, that may be independent variables correlated with dependent variables, such as increased academic performance, following intervention. To the degree the researcher is explicit in the operations used to select the sample and has provided adequate sample description, the probability of direct or systematic replication increases.

This issue has been a particular problem in research in NBD. Exclusion and inclusion criteria are often not made explicit. Generally, the sample description goes no further than a statement that the children were learning disabled as defined by the schools, with a report of estimates of intelligence, the sex distribution and age (see, for example, Ayres, 1972b, 1978; Gregory-Flock & Yerxa, 1984; Ottenbacher, Short & Watson, 1979).

Sampling Issues

Given the need to adequately identify, select, and describe subjects, children with NBD present some unique sampling problems. Children can be referred from a variety of sources that may influence both assessment and treatment variables. Having problems in neurobehavioral functions may result in a child being referred for evaluation and treatment from a general practitioner, psychiatrist, psychologist, neurologist or from various facilities such as a developmental disabilities clinic, pediatric department or a class for learning disabled. To the degree a sample is made up, in part or completely, of such referrals, there is the possibility of some variable acting systematically on outcome. The issues are random selection from a population in order to obtain a representative sample, as well as to control for any unknown independent variables by having them randomly distributed among the subjects. Frequently, the number of subjects used in neurobehavioral research is relatively small, poorly described, and possibly open to systematic bias.

The possible systematic bias of sex and age factors are not unique to neurobehavioral research since this is found in much of the research on learning disabilities. However, the sampling problem of the disproportionate number of males to females may introduce a unique problem. One of the characteristics of this population is poor equilibrium and uncoordinated behavior and these are behaviors that are generally socially undesirable when found in males. This may result in more behavioral problems occurring in males in a sample and raises problems of population representation and generalization of findings.

The effects of attrition on sample representation is particularly important to monitor and report in research on intervention. To be effective, sensory-integration therapy must be given over a period of time, and some attrition in both experimental and control groups might be expected. However, attrition rate may be systematic and affect results. For example, children coming from lower social economic status (SES) families might be expected to have a higher rate of attrition because of stressful family circumstances such as single parent status, or factors such as acceptance and then disruption of treatment. If a variable found frequently in lower SES families, such as low language skills and reading comprehension, influences the dependent variables used to measure the response to treatment, then systematic high attrition rates in this group could certainly influence outcome and generalization of results.

It is interesting to note that the major studies on the effects of sensory integration therapy do not report any attrition or quantitative description of the SES or racial background of the sample of children used in the research (Ayres, 1972b, 1978; Ottenbacher et al., 1979).

Control and Comparison Groups

The logic behind using various groups to compare with a sample characterized as being unique in terms of some dimension of NBD is based in part on clinical experience. With experience the clinician observes a pattern of responses, such as hyponystagmus and poor equilibrium reactions, that is consistently related to some other behavior, such as learning disabilities. On the basis of accumulated observations, the clinician then makes the prediction that whenever this unique pattern occurs in a child then the child will also demonstrate learning disabilities. To validate an assessment procedure, the target behavior must be specified and measured reliably. The next step is to relate the target behavior to some meaningful criterion. In research using the criterion group membership design, the clinician's logic, if behavior A, then membership in group B, is reversed: group B, membership in a learning disabled population will result in behavior A, hyponystagmus or poor equilibrium reactions. Obviously, the logic of the clinician, in the context of discovery, is not reversible in the context of confirmation, where groups are heterogeneous (Sines, 1964). However, even if the assessment procedure is reliable, if it cannot discriminate in a scientifically sound and clinically meaningful way between subgroups in the criterion population, the procedure has limited utility.

Actually, there has been very little research on the distribution of signs of NBD in different contrast groups or among subgroups of the learning disabled population. This is a major shortcoming especially when there are procedures that are presented as being clinically useful in the assessment of NBD in learning disabled children (Ayres,

1980, p. 6). The studies that have been done will be presented in more detail later. What follows is an outline of suggested research using contrast and control groups. Comparisons between LD children demonstrating signs of NBD and a contrast group with NBD showing no academic problems would be important in contributing to the establishment of a more functional relationship between NBD and learning disabilities. A difficulty in finding such a contrast group would in itself be interesting. A comparison of such a NBD group and LD-NBD group with a normal group, probably best done in an educational setting, would answer questions about NBD such as its contribution to behavior problems. Comparison between the three samples in terms of the distribution of signs of NBD would add important information regarding the equivocal or nonequivocal status of the signs (Morrison, 1982). A variation of this design is to control for the severity of NBD signs to form subgroups within the NBD and LD samples. In this quasi-experimental design, the level of NBD would be used as an independent variable and the relationship with various dependent variables, such as level or type of reading retardation, would be investigated. The comparisons could be within the NBD subgroups as well as contrast LD groups negative for NBD.

Studies of control and contrast groups such as these would contribute to our knowledge of the value of procedures used to assess NBD and the contribution of NBD to learning disabilities. Turning to intervention, a similar logic regarding the use of a design involving the severity of signs of NBD and treatment could be useful. Such a design would have to include a no contact-control group for each level of severity. The power in interpreting results would be increased significantly by addition of equated groups receiving some other form of treatment and/or social attention. Studies of the effects of sensory integration therapy will be examined more closely in what follows. A number of these studies have the weakness of not having an adequate control group design.

The use of control-contrast groups for either purposes of the investigation of NBD itself, or the effects of intervention on NBD and learning disabilities must include more measures, particularly behavioral measures, than has been true in the past. This is necessary to equate the groups in terms of background variables such as intelligence, previous treatment, and SES, and to make more explicit the inclusion and exclusion criterion used in selection. Behavioral measures such as general level of behavior disturbance, hyperactivity and/or attention deficit disorder may be included as measures for equating groups but also serve as study variables. The issues regarding the selection and measurement of dependent-independent variables, as well as the interrelated issues of poor sample description, have been the major weakness of research in NBD.

Independent-Dependent Variables

A sign of dysfunction, in this example, hyponystagmus, illustrates some of the measurement issues typical of this field. Although it is possible to measure nystagmus with rather precise instrumentation by electronystagmography, the procedure has considerable practical limitations except when used in a laboratory setting. The most often used procedure is to estimate nystagmus duration by observation. In practice this is somewhat difficult to do, especially in judging when nystagmus actually stops. Research has demonstrated that with an LD population nystagmus duration is more variable at testing, and from one test to another, than is true of duration in a normal comparison group. Any experiment with LD children using nystagmus duration as either a matching variable, independent variable, or dependent variable, requires major consideration by the researcher of the reliability parameters of this measure. Many of the behaviors used as signs of NBD, such as the tonic neck reflexes and equilibrium adjustments, have the characteristics of having to be measured by observation, and of being variable over time.

In any study of intervention, variables other than the signs of NBD should be measured, especially because of their possible contribution as independent variables. An independent variable, measured or unmeasured, is relevant if it affects any outcome variable. This may occur by the variable acting alone or, as is probably most often the case, interacting with other variables. In the major studies of the effect of sensory integration therapy, the dependent variable has either been academic progress (Ayres, 1972b, 1978) or change in nystagmus duration (Ottenbacher et al., 1979) Sensory integration therapy is assumed to affect NBD and academic performance but there may be other variables related to academic performance that are modified by sensory integration therapy, or equally modified by other interventions. Attention deficit disorder and/or hyperactivity are known to occur frequently in the LD population (Knights & Bakker, 1980). Depending on definition and sampling, estimates vary but range from 10-25%. It is certainly possible that attention deficit problems and/or hyperactivity would occur frequently in any group of LD children either being assessed for NBD or being treated by some form of therapy for NBD and/or learning disability. If the therapy modifies the attention-concentration problem, one would expect some positive outcome in academic performance. Crucial in the design of such studies is the measurement of potential independent variables. For example, if after a period of therapy, there is a positive change in attention and hyperactivity measures and academic performance, with no change in the signs of NBD, then one has a better basis for evaluating the variables that are being modified by the intervention.

Analysis of Data

In the typical assessment or treatment study of NBD, many more measures should be obtained, reported, and analyzed in the results. Attempts to enumerate all relevant independent and dependent variables will probably be impossible, but knowledge of the field will enable a researcher to attend to the major ones. Various strategies may be used to address the issue of the possible effects of independent variables but all have in common some level of quantification. There are four major strategies: (1) investigate children with only one level of the variable, restricting its range and controlling it by exclusion; (2) assign children to groups so that each group is equated for the variable; (3) employ statistical techniques, such as analysis of covariance, to test for the effect of the variable; (4) enter the variable into the design as an independent variable to test its effect (Loney & Halmi, 1980).

The need to include more than one dependent variable creates numerous problems in data analysis. In intervention studies, measures should be included that can show both positive and negative effects of intervention in both academic and social behaviors. The major interpretive problems come from the inclusion of an array of relevant outcome measures and the increased probability of finding a significant difference between the intervention and control-contrast groups when none actually exists. The issues related to multiple outcome measures and problems in inflated Type 1 error have received considerable attention. The use of MANOVA procedures are generally accepted as a reasonable method of analysis (Leary & Altmarer, 1980). MANOVA may reduce the chances of detecting significance under some conditions (Type II error), but it has also been shown to be powerful for detecting real experimental effects that occur across more than one dependent variable (Larrabee, 1982). Although the technique has been recommended for studies using multiple dependent variables for some time (Overall & Klett, 1972), MANOVA has only been used in the analysis of the results of one study of the effects of sensory integration therapy with NBD children (Carte, Morrison, Sublett, Uemura & Setrakian, 1984).

Adequate measurement and reporting of relevant variables are important for establishing useful assessment procedures and are also important for the establishment of useful methods of intervention. Issues concerning subject selection, description, sampling and analysis of results as they relate to research in NBD, are best illustrated by examining two typical studies, one in the area of assessment and the other in the area of intervention.

Assessment

There is a considerable advantage in being able to diagnose more precisely within a general syndrome. Based on medical practice, greater diagnostic precision can have significance for both prognosis and treatment. Some attempt has been made to broaden the diagnostic and clinical significance of vestibular dysfunction in LD children by investigating the relationship of nystagmus duration to degree of neuropsychological dysfunction. Previous research on vestibular dysfunction has indicated that LD children with prolonged nystagmus duration appeared to have more extensive neurological involvement. To examine this relationship more closely, the Southern California Sensory Integration Test (SCSIT) developed by Ayres (1980) and the Southern California Postrotary Nystagmus Test (PNT), also developed by Ayres (1975), were given to 109 children described as having learning disabilities (Ottenbacher, 1980). The details of the study will not be presented here, but the results were interpreted as showing that (1) LD children judged to have relatively greater neuropsychological involvement exhibited longer postrotary nystagmus duration; (2) tests from the SCSIT measuring cortical level functions shared significant variance with prolonged nystagmus duration scores; and (3) depressed nystagmus scores were significantly related to poor equilibrium adjustments. Because of inadequate subject description and sampling procedures, and the use of measures with unacceptable or unknown reliability characteristics, these results cannot be accepted with confidence.

One of the major difficulties is the age range of the sample and the inadequate criteria used to define learning disabilities. In the group of 34 children having more neurological involvement, the age range was from 58 to 116 months, with the mean age being 86.27, SD = 18.21. Assuming a normal distribution within this group, half of the population, or seventeen children, were less than eighty-six months old, and approximately three of this group were less than sixty-eight months old. Examination of the total sample suggests that perhaps half of the sample was made up of children who may be in kindergarten or entering first grade. These children may be at-risk for academic learning failure but are not learning disabled children by the usual criterion (Lerner, 1981).

A related issue is the inadequate description of the population: "All subjects had medical and educational diagnoses of learning disability ..." (Ottenbacher, 1980, p. 41). A medical diagnosis *and* an educational diagnosis are not the same since the former would certainly use medical criteria whereas the latter could only use educational criteria. The fact that approximately half of the sample of 109 were either in kindergarten or had not completed the first grade strongly suggests that educational criteria for LD could not have been used. A more precise criterion for LD might have helped with such a young sample. For example, a significant discrepancy between intelligence and expected academic achievement could have been used as an operational definition of learning disability, although testing for academic achievement has limited meaning until the end of first or second grade.

The issues in measurement are related to the use of nystagmus duration and equilibrium reactions. As noted earlier, the assessment of these signs is based on observation and can be influenced by the various factors that determine human perception and interpretation of events. This situation requires that a researcher give adequate attention to, and control of, such basics as inter- and intra-scorer reliability. This study provides no such data regarding PNT, and examination of the data suggests that this may be a problem. Comparisons of the standard deviations for Group 1, the neurologically involved sample, and Group 2, the less neurologically involved, indicate that there is more variability in both groups than found in a normal population. For example, examination of Table 1, p. 83, of the data provided by Punwar (1982) indicates that the standard deviation of a compar-

42

able normal sample is 5.79, while the children in this study in Group 1 had an SD = 17.12 and children in Group 2 had an SD = 10.70. In fact, the Group 2 standard deviation is 1.08 sec. less than the mean. This suggests that the total sample had more variance in scores than did a normal sample and therefore their individual scores may be less reliable. An investigation of the reliability of PNT in a sample of reading retarded children of average intelligence demonstrated that LD children's scores were less reliable than those reported in normal samples (Morrison & Sublett, 1983). Another issue related to measurement in Ottenbacher's study is the definition of prolonged nystagmus. The mean PNT duration score reported for Group 1 is 23.06 sec. The mean PNT duration score for a comparable normal sample is 21.78 sec. It is difficult to accept an operational definition of prolonged duration as having pathological implications if it also occurs in a sample having no academic problems.

Finally, the conclusion that a relationship exists between equilibrium reactions and depressed nystagmus is based on a regression analysis showing shared variance between depressed PNT scores and standing balance as measured by the SCSIT. The issues regarding reliability of PNT scores are pertinent to this conclusion as well, but the measure of equilibrium has similar problems. Standing balance with eyes open and then with eyes closed is the measure of equilibrium adjustments used by Ottenbacher in his analysis. Test retest reliability for standing balance with eyes open has adequate stability. However, of the three estimates reported for standing balance tested with eyes closed for the age range used in this study, two did not reach statistical significance (Ayres, 1980, Table 80).

Intervention

In a study of the effects of sensory integration (SI) therapy in a group of 23 LD children having hyponystagmus, Ayres (1978) found improved academic performance following six months of therapy given once a week for one half hour. A no-contact control received their special classroom instruction during the same interval. Again, the results of this study cannot be accepted with confidence because of limitations in experimental design.

The original sample of 92 children were simply selected from "children in special public school classes in the southwestern part of Los Angeles County" (Ayres, 1978, p. 32). No data is provided regarding

43

the research criteria for original selection as a learning disabled sample other than this statement. A variety of academic tests were given both pre- and post-intervention but no data is reported that would indicate either the level or type of learning disability. The issue of sample selection becomes more important because the school system itself used two criteria: (1) academic achievement below intellectual capacity or (2) inability of the child with average or above average intelligence to profit from standard classroom experience. In this latter group behavioral factors were often involved in the criterion. There are no figures given to indicate how many children this may be. This presents serious limitations in terms of interpretation of outcome. Behavioral problems are known to exist so it cannot be zero influence, but no measures of behavior disturbance or related behaviors such as attention-concentration and/or hyperactivity were obtained. Since this is an intervention study it is important to demonstrate the degree to which outcome variables might be related to these behavior variables. As it stands, these behaviors could be independent variables or behaviors that covary with the outcome variables.

A major weakness in this study is the use of tests as either criterion variables or dependent variables with no reporting of data such as means or standard deviations. The PNT duration scores are used to identify the two hyponystagmus groups but there is no way to tell what the scores were except that they were obtained from children who scored -1.1 SD or lower. It is unclear whether or not this is below the mean of this sample or the mean of a normal population. It is possible that the score used as an indicator of hyponystagmus is in the range of nystagmus scores found in a normal sample as was the case of the hypernystagmus score in the Ottenbacher study. A major interpretation issue occurs because no pre-post intervention nystagmus scores are presented. Since SI therapy is presented as being effective for vestibular dysfunction, some measure of change in vestibular dysfunction has to be presented. Nystagmus duration could be seen as a dependent variable with change in scores from abnormally low to the average range reflecting the effects of SI therapy. No change in any vestibular function is reported. This is a major problem since no group was used that might control for the effects of added social attention or the Hawthorn effect.

A related problem is the use of three subtests of the WRAT as dependent variables without reporting basic information such as the means, standard deviation, and range. Change scores on these three subtests were compared with the median change score for both groups combined. A chi-square analysis applied to the number of children in each group falling above or below the median indicated that more children experiencing SI therapy showed positive academic change (p < .05). Besides the WRAT, portions of the ITPA, the Flowers-Costello Tests of Central Auditory Abilities and the Slossom Oral Reading Test were given pre- and post- intervention. Separate analysis was performed on some of these tests but failed to demonstrate any pre-post difference between the two groups. This is a study using multiple dependent variables in which MANOVA might have made a significant contribution to the analysis of the data. Using a median change analysis of three academic subtests that were part of a battery of academic measures increases the probability of Type 1 error in the interpretation of results.

Conclusion

It would seem that during the initial period of time in which scientists attempt to confirm observations, there is a tendency to answer the simplest questions, such as does the behavior exist? Or how does x relate to y in a correlational analysis? If there is sufficient confirmation at this level, then more complex research occurs where the parameters of the behavior are established and multiple variables are measured and analyzed. The issues regarding research on NBD are not unique but occur in most areas of the behavioral sciences. Solutions to the problems can be found by the application of scientifically sound principles of research.

At this point in time research is certainly moving past the point of initial confirmation and more complex designs can be used to answer questions regarding such issues as the relationship between NBD and perceptual processing dysfunctions and the existence of discrete syndromes in NBD. The research that has been criticized in the previous discussion has made significant contributions to our knowledge even though there were limitations in the methodology and design. Contributions to an area of research can come from a variety of activities other than research itself. For example, Jean Ayres has probably had more positive influence on clinical practice and research in NBD than any individual over the last decade. She clearly has served to attract the attention and interest of many clinicians and researchers. She has done this as much through her clinical skills as a diagnostician and therapist as she has through her contribution to research. In the review to follow it will become clear that a considerable amount of solid research has already occurred and that there is a firm scientific base for future research efforts in NBD. Perhaps the forgoing critique of previous research will contribute in some way to the generation of more research that will answer questions regarding the etiology, evaluation, development over time and treatment of neurobehavioral and perceptual dysfunctions in children with learning disabilities.

Chapter 5

Tonic Neck Reflexes

Introduction

When an infant between birth and six months or so sleeps in the prone position, the limbs on the face-side tend to extend while the limbs on the skull-side flex. This is the so called "fencer position" and is caused by the change in muscle tone contingent upon the movement and position of the infant's head. This is an involuntary reflex and the eliciting stimulus is the infant's own movements. A less commonly observed reflex occurs during this same period of time when the infant's head moves down or up. By tilting the head down, the muscle tone in the arms cause the arms to flex while the muscle tone in the legs results in extension. Moving the head up produces the opposite change in muscle tone in the arms and legs.

The tonic neck reflexes may have some adaptive value in early infancy. For example, they can serve to automatically align the infant's head for feeding and perhaps decrease the hazards of suffocation. However, they can also have a negative effect in the development of voluntary motor coordination and visual-motor integration. As the name suggests, the limbs are influenced by the movement of the head and the muscle tone is maintained as long as the head is in a rotated position. In the normal sequence of development, the contingency between head movement and muscle tone in the arms and legs becomes voluntary rather than involuntary. However, there is evidence that tonic neck reflexes persist beyond the period of time normally observed in learning-disabled children. Two such reflexes, the asymmetric and symmetric tonic neck reflexes, have received considerable attention from both clinicians and researchers.

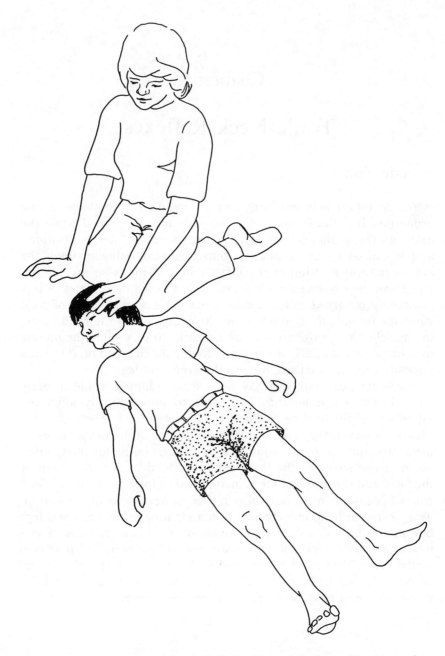

Figure 1: Asymmetric Tonic Neck Reflex-Dorsal Position. Head turned to side; no observable change in legs or arms. Normal response.

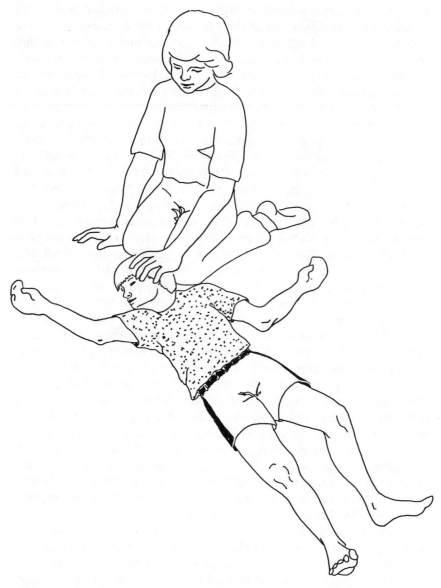

Figure 2:   Asymmetric Tonic Neck Reflex-Dorsal Position. Head turned to side; observable extension of arm and leg on face side and observable flexion of limbs on occiput-side. Non-adaptive inhibition of reflex.

Asymmetric Tonic Neck Reflex (ATNR)

At the most subtle clinical level the ATNR is observed with head rotation with no movement of the extremities but a change in muscle tone with increased extension on the face side and a corresponding increased flexion on the occiput-side. In the more pronounced cases, as illustrated in Figure 2, there are varying degrees of movement in the extremities with the arm and leg on the face side extending and a corresponding flexion on the opposite side.

The possible connection between CNS pathology and the tonic neck reflexes is based on observations that animals deprived of their labyrinths demonstrated postsurgical occurrences of these reflexes and that children with known CNS pathology also demonstrated these reflexes to varying degrees (Bobath, 1971; Magnus, 1926). The relationship between the ATNR and pathology is also strengthened by the observation that normal infants of four weeks of age spontaneously assume the ATNR position but by twenty weeks the reflex is difficult to elicit (Gessell, 1940). This suggests that the ATNR is a normal occurrence only if it can be elicited during early infancy and that its persistence, or recurrence, in later development is indicative of retardation, and/or a prognostic indicator of future problems in motor development (Capute et al., 1978). Further evidence for the value of the ATNR as a sign of CNS pathology is obtained by studies demonstrating that the ATNR was difficult to elicit in a group of normal infants after three months but could be produced in 90% of an abnormal group of infants after the age of six months (Paine, 1964). These were clinical studies based on observation of the reflex by an individual clinician doing the evaluation. Although the clinical studies are consistent in the general finding that the late occurrence of the ATNR is a sign of pathology, there is evidence that the evaluation procedures might be less than precise. For example, one clinical study found that the ATNR could be elicited in only 60% of 108 normal newborns and that the chances of observing the reflex on one trial was 3/16 (Vassella & Karlsson, 1962).

Interpreting the late occurrence of the ATNR as a sign of CNS pathology was challenged by the demonstration that with more precise measurement the reflex could be found in normal male subjects between the ages of 7 to 10 and up to 25 years of age. Maturation contributes to the occurrence of the ATNR over this age range with younger males demonstrating the reflex with more intensity than older males (Ikai, 1950). There is good evidence that the ATNR may be elicited in children demonstrating no known CNS pathology or learning problems. In a sample of 84 normal children evaluated in the quadruped position the ATNR was elicited in all children between the ages of 3 to 9 years (Parr, Routh & Byrd, 1974). There is also evidence that the occurrence of the ATNR in later development is not necessarily a sign of pathology but rather a sign of normal neurophysiological function. The ATNR contributes to the supportive framework in nonstressful movement but can be elicited more intensely under stress conditions, such as heavy exercise, with inhibition being demonstrated once stress is reduced (Easton, 1972). The ATNR is normally elicited contingent to movements of the shoulder girdle and upper limbs. With the stress of intense exercise the reflex occurs more strongly. This appears to be an adaptive function, rather than a pathological function, of the ATNR, with rotation of the head toward the exercising side being facilitory.

A major question concerning the ATNR is the distribution of the reflex and/or the intensity of its occurrence in pathological and nonpathological samples. Previous clinical observation has indicated that children with behavior problems and reading retardation demonstrated the ATNR when tested in the standing position. During this evaluation there was pronounced elbow flexion on the occiput side during passive rotation of the head (Silver, 1952). When tested in the supine position, 25% of a learning disabled sample demonstrated the ATNR while the reflex could be elicited in only 3% of a sample of normal children (Rider, 1972). In another clinical study testing in the quadruped position, boys demonstrating inadequate postural adjustments and behavior problems demonstrated the ATNR more intensely than did a group of normal boys (Finocchario, 1974). However, in another study a clinical evaluation failed to elicit the ATNR in either a normal or a behavioral disturbed sample of children attending regular classrooms (Rider, 1973).

Symmetric Tonic Neck Reflex (STNR)

This reflex has received considerable clinical study and is considered as an important part of the standard pediatric neurological evaluation (Capute et al., 1978). In infancy the evaluation is done by holding the subject in the prone sitting position. As the head is either actively or passively flexed or extended at body midline, there is a corresponding change in the muscle tone of the limbs. In the extreme case, exten-

51

sion of the head results in the arms extending with legs in flexion, while head flexion has the opposite effect; the arms flex and the legs extend (Capute et al., 1978, pp. 44-45). Clinical experience indicates that the STNR is fairly subtle in the normal infant and this has resulted is some discrepancies in the reported incidences of the reflex. Assessment of the STNR in older children is made difficult by the practical problems of placing the child in a position suitable to elicit the reflex. One solution to this problem is to test the child in the prone position over the examiner's lap while the head is flexed or extended at midline (Morrison et al., 1978, p. 123). This allows the limbs to hang freely and contingent movement with the head to be observed. However, experience has demonstrated that this procedure has limited utility as the child grows and is too tall or heavy to be tested comfortably.

It is often stated that the STNR replaces the ATNR and permits bilateral and midline activities. However, clinical observations indicate that the two reflexes can be elicited during the first year of life (Capute et al., 1978), and there is no research to indicate that there is a sequence or that one is more intense than the other. There is also research indicating that like the ATNR, the STNR can be elicited in normal adults in both stressful and nonstressful conditions. It would appear that the tonic reflexes continue to exist and exert an adaptive influence beyond the first year of life. It is more than likely that one does not replace the other but that both continue to contribute in a positive way to body posture and movement through adulthood (Easton, 1972).

The Tonic Neck Reflexes as Signs of CNS Pathology

It is not possible to interpret the simple occurrence of a tonic neck reflex beyond the first year of life as an indicator of neuropathology. More precise methods of observation and measurement suggest that the reflex can function in an adaptive rather than a pathological way, in body posture and movement. Electromyographic studies of muscle contraction in response to head rotation under laboratory conditions have contributed significantly to our knowledge of the adaptive role of the tonic neck reflex. The fact that the reflex can be elicited in normal children as well as in children showing behavior problems and/or learning disabilities suggests that it is an equivocal sign of neuropathology. The mere occurrence of the tonic neck reflex in isolation would never be considered a sign of neuropathology but its occurrence with other primitive reflexes and inadequate postural adjustments would contribute to such an interpretation. The diagnostic value of the sign itself as part of a syndrome or pattern would have to be established by some other measure than occurrence or nonoccurrence. Clinical assessments of the tonic neck reflex probably always involve an evaluation of the quality or intensity of the reflex. This evaluation may be implicit and based on the internal norms of the evaluator. It may be that the tonic neck reflex can be elicited in normal as well as pathological samples but that it is the frequency, duration, or intensity of the reflex that discriminates between the two samples.

A related issue is the lack of consistent procedures used to elicit the reflex and measure its occurrence. The need to develop standardized methods of observation and measurement have been recognized and efforts have been made to develop such methods for infants (Capute et al., 1978) and latency-aged children (Parmenter, 1983; Pothier, Friedlander, Morrison & Herman, 1983). Some of the inconsistent data regarding when the reflex is more suppressed in normal children or less inhibited in pathological samples may be due to the various procedures used to elicit the reflex. For example, children have been assessed for the ATNR in one trial in the supine position (Rider, 1972), in the quadruped position with a variety of head rotations (Finocchario, 1974; Parmenter, 1975), standing with voluntary and involuntary head rotation (Silver, 1952), or three different positions with involuntary head movement (Sieg & Shuster, 1979). There is evidence that the ATNR can be influenced by a variety of stress factors related to position of the child while being tested.

Assessment of the ATNR

The focus here will be on the procedures used to assess the ATNR in latency-aged children rather than infancy. The former age range is selected for the reason that this is the range in which the learning disabled child is typically found. The procedures to be discussed are also generally suitable for pre-kindergarten and kindergarten-aged children who may be at-risk for the development of learning disabilities. A review of the relevant literature indicates that four positions have been used most frequently to assess the ATNR: dorsal, standing, quadruped and the quadruped reflex inhibiting posture. As a general principle, no matter what the position, the child must not be dressed in such a way so as to obscure observation of the change in muscle tone and movement in the limbs contingent upon head rotation.

To test in the dorsal position, the child should be on a comfortable surface with the head in the midline position and arms and legs extended. The evaluation can be done with the head passively rotated by the examiner and/or voluntarily rotated. In the latter case the child must comprehend the request. Since the head should be rotated consistently in terms of number of rotations and distance rotated, the use of voluntary rotation presents certain methodological problems. The behavior to be observed is the change in muscle tone or movement with extension being elicited as the head is turned and maintained in position on the face side and flexion being elicited on the occiput-side.

In the standing position, the child should be on a level surface in his bare feet with the weight evenly distributed. The head should be at midline with arms outstretched and parallel to the floor. The fingers are abducted. The focus of observation, except in pronounced cases of pathology, is usually the change in tone and movement of the extended arms. The longer the arms are held in this position the more stressful the situation. With a child in such stress the ATNR might be more easily elicited, but there may be a confounding effect of muscle fatigue.

The quadruped position adds a degree of stress, particularly to the arms, not found in the dorsal position. Again, as is true in the standing position, too long an interval for testing may add the confounding effect of muscle fatigue. Placed on a stable and level surface, the child's weight is evenly distributed over the four limbs. The fingers should be even and forward while the elbows are extended but not locked at the joints to provide support. With the head in the midline, rotation can be obtained by either voluntary or passive control. As illustrated in Figure 4, the flexion of the elbow appears to be the most sensitive indicator of the ATNR with varying degrees of flexion on the occiput side being observed contingent upon head movement.

The quadruped reflex inhibiting position (QRIP) requires that the child comprehend considerable verbal instruction or be able to imitate the examiner's modeling. On a level surface the child's weight is evenly distributed on the four limbs. By either tactile or verbal cues the child is instructed to put his hand on one hip while the opposite leg is lifted off the floor. Upon instruction or tactile cue, the child is

Figure 3: Asymmetric Tonic Neck Reflex-Quadruped Position. Head turned to side; no observable change in arms. Normal response.

Figure 4: Asymmetric Tonic Neck Reflex-Quadruped Position. Head turned to side; observable extension of arm on face side and observable flexion of arm on occiput-side. Non-adaptive inhibition of reflex.

then to rotate the head actively to the left and right (Ayres, 1972a, p. 106). Under this stressed position, flexion or extension is frequently accompanied by loss of balance.

Tonic Neck Reflex and Bodily Stress

The distribution and magnitude of the tonic neck reflexes as a function of such factors as age and normal versus pathological subsamples of children is an area in need of research. Previous interpretations that the occurrence of the reflex after the first year of life is a sign, among other neurological signs, of possible neuropathology needs to be examined more closely. As has been noted, some of the problems in interpreting the occurrence of the tonic neck reflex is that various investigators have employed a range of techniques to evaluate the reflex. Clinical experiences suggest that the position of the body during the elicitation affects the frequency and intensity of the reflex. Considering the ATNR, besides position affecting the reflex, other procedures that may affect the occurrence are moving the head actively or passively, maintaining the head in the rotated position for varying lengths of time, testing with eyes open or closed, including muscle tone change in the scoring system, and discriminating between voluntary and involuntary muscle tone change and/or movement of limbs. To the degree that the ATNR can be considered as one sign of NBD in LD children that may have clinical significance, observational techniques and related evaluation procedures have to be well described and standardized. The history of interpreting the ATNR as a clinical sign of CNS dysfunction is considerable and the empirical data for such an association is impressive. However, recent research with the LD population indicates that more attention needs to be given to the effect of body position in eliciting the ATNR for the reflex to be considered a sign occurring more frequently or intensely in this population than in other contrast groups.

The concurrent validity of the ATNR as a sign of CNS dysfunction is questioned by research demonstrating that the reflex can be elicited in children having no academic problems. Using the quadruped position to evaluate a normal sample, Parmenter (1975), established that visible muscle tone changes or elbow flexion to 30% ipsilateral to the skull position could be elicited in children seven to nine years of age. On a six point scale measuring both muscle tone and elbow flexion, younger children demonstrated more observable signs of the reflex than did the older subgroup. The scale used a scoring system based on observed changes in flexion and extension of muscle tone as well as limb movement. Obvious elbow flexion on the occiput-side was measured by a goniometer while slight elbow flexion and muscle tone change were judged by sight. Details are not provided on the procedures used to establish the interrater reliability of the scoring system of .95. The scale has been subsequently revised to a four point system with guidelines provided for interpretation (Parmenter, 1983).

The need for more systematic measurement of the ATNR to establish its concurrent validity is highlighted by research supporting the clinical observation that the position used to assess the reflex is a factor to be considered in the interpretation of its occurrence (Sieg & Shuster, 1979). This research is also pertinent because the sample of children used as subjects were learning disabled. However, no details are provided regarding the sample except that there were 24 males between the ages of 8 to 11. Three different positions were used to evaluate the ATNR: (1) quadruped with head passively rotated from side to side, (2) standing with eyes closed and head passively rotated from side to side with the arms outstretched, and (3) quadruped reflex inhibiting posture. The results of independent evaluations observed by film indicated that if the reflex was observed in one position there was a high probability that it would be observed in the other two. Evaluations in the standing position resulted in more normal ratings than the other two positions whereas these two did not differ in terms of normal ratings. Testing in the quadruped inhibiting position produced more ratings in the abnormal category than did evaluations in the other two positions. These results strongly suggest that the quadruped inhibiting position is more stressful than the other two positions and may be a better position to elicit the ATNR. Whether or not this would be true with a better defined LD sample or is a function of such factors as age or overall severity of NBD is an empirical question to be a addressed by research. One of the limitations of this study, besides the inadequate sample description, is that a three category system of scoring was used by three different evaluators. The three categories were abnormal, questionable and normal. Insufficient data is provided regarding the interrater reliability of the scoring system.

Distribution of the Tonic Neck Reflex in LD Children

The previous research suggests that the stress of the position used to assess the tonic neck reflex is an important factor in the evaluation procedure. A related issue in assessment is the occurrence of the reflex in different populations. Of particular interest are the parameters of the reflex in LD children who are negative for the usual signs of CNS pathology. If assessment variables are adequately controlled for, the demonstration of this reflex in this sample, either in terms of frequency, duration or intensity, in comparison to meaningful contrast groups, would contribute to the predictive validity of the sign as pathonomic. A number of investigators have moved in the direction of evaluating the intensity or degree of occurrence (Capute et al., 1978; Parmenter, 1983; Pothier et al., 1983).

The Primitive Reflex and Postural Adjustment Procedure (PRPA) is a behavioral-based technique for evaluation of the tonic neck reflex as well as a variety of posture reactions and equilibrium adjustments (Pothier et al. 1983). The tonic neck reflex is assessed in the dorsal and quadruped position for the ATNR and by having the child lie across the examiner's lap in the prone position for the STNR. As noted earlier, clinical experience indicates that the STNR cannot be reliably assessed in this latter position in children much beyond eight years of age. Since this limits the assessment of the STNR in many children identified as not achieving at academic level, the data on this procedure will not be discussed here. To evaluate the ATNR in the dorsal position the child's head is passively rotated by the examiner five times, briefly pausing at the end of each rotation as close to the child's shoulder as possible without making the child uncomfortable. In the quadruped position the head is rotated using the same procedure. In the dorsal position the head is rotated by the examiner situated just behind the child's head, while in the quadruped position the examiner is situated to the child's left or right and behind the shoulders. The scoring system ranges from 0 to 3 and is based on contingent flexion and extension of the limbs with the rotation of the head. Pilot studies indicated that it was not possible to reliably score change in muscle tone by unaided visual observation. The degree of movement is quantified from 0, no observable movement, through mild and moderate occurrence, to 3 which is extreme extension of any limb on the face-side and/or flexion of any limb on the occiput-side. In the quadruped position, the elbow flexion on the occiput-side is the most reliable measure of the ATNR.

58

The ATNR may be evaluated in the dorsal or quadruped position on the PRPA and may also be assessed more indirectly by body righting. In body righting the child is placed on a four foot wide mat and rolls approximately eight feet toward an object at the end of the mat. After reaching the object, the child then rolls back to the beginning point. Segmental coordinated rolling is scored 0; mildly uncoordinated rolling is scored 1; moderately uncoordinated rolling is scored 2; while extremely uncoordinated rolling is scored 3. Observation indicates that rolling adds considerable body stress to children with inadequately inhibited tonic neck reflexes. The need to rotate the head as well as flex and extend it during rolling elicits both the STNR and ATNR resulting in inadequate body righting and poorly coordinated rolling. The exception to this is seen in the child with poor muscle tone who may have difficulty rolling because of hypotonicity. Except with children with observable hypotonicity, the combined scores for the ATNR and Body Righting can be used as a measure of the tonic neck reflex in the PRPA.

The interrater reliability of this procedure has been established with a normal, mentally retarded and LD sample of children (Morrison, 1982). Estimates were obtained by having an evaluator and an observer independently score an assessment of the ATNR. For the mentally retarded group (N = 14), this produced a r = .67 (p = .004), and for the normal sample (N = 19) a r = .80 (p = .001). For the LD sample, this produced a reliability estimate of r = .85 (p > .001). The LD children were 86.2 months old and were enrolled in special programs for the learning disabled. They had average intelligence as measured by the WISC-R, and independent evaluations of reading decoding and comprehension demonstrated signficant discrepancies between intelligence and reading achievement. As a group they were a standard deviation below the expected level of reading comprehension for their age. The nineteen children used in the study were part of a larger sample of eighty-seven children (Carte et al., 1984). This smaller subgroup was selected to be matched and compared on the ATNR with the mentally retarded and normal samples. Statistical comparisons demonstrated that the LD subsample did not differ from the large sample in terms of NBD, intelligence or academic achievement. The data was analyzed by multiple range test comparisons between the nineteen LD children and the matched sample of mentally retarded and normal children. This analysis established that assessing the ATNR in the dorsal position elicited the reflex to a greater degree in the mentally retarded children than in the LD and normal sample who did not differ when assessed in this position. However, when the ATNR was evaluated in the quadruped position, the mentally retarded and LD children demonstrated an equal degree of the reflex and a greater degree than did the normal children. A similar result was found with the assessment of body righting where the mentally retarded and LD children were the same and scored significantly more in the pathological direction than did the normal children (Morrison, 1982).

The results of this study contribute to the concurrent validity of the ATNR as a pathonomic sign in a number of ways. Mentally retarded children are known to demonstrate pathological reflex development (Zapella et al., 1964), poor equilibrium reactions, and delays in motor development (Molnar, 1978) as well as CNS pathology (Khanna, 1973). The finding that the LD children demonstrated similar levels of reflex pathology in two of the three evaluation procedures suggests that some level of CNS dysfunction may be contributing to the LD child's academic problems. The failure to elicit the ATNR to the same degree in the normal sample, when compared to the other children in two of the assessments, strongly supports the argument that it is the magnitude of the late occurrence of the ATNR that is the pathonomic sign. Finally, the results support previous research (Sieg & Shuster, 1979) demonstrating the effect of position in eliciting the tonic neck reflex and suggest an interaction effect between reflex pathology and assessment procedure. If the ATNR had been assessed only in the dorsal position, the LD sample would not have been discriminated from the normal children, although the mentally retarded children would have been shown to have an abnormal reflex. Evaluating the ATNR in the quadruped position and by body righting established that the LD and mentally retarded sample were from the same population, as far as reflex pathology was concerned, while the added stress of the two procedures did not change the status of the normal children.

Conclusion

As is true of most of the research to be discussed in this text, knowledge of the tonic neck reflex and its contributions to both adaptive and non-adaptive development will be increased by further systematic research. The data indicating that the reflex does occur to a greater degree in LD children than in children having no academic problems is in need of research efforts at direct, as well as systematic, replication. Rather than assuming that the failure to adequately inhibit the tonic neck reflex may have some relationship to lack of cerebral dominance (deQuiros & Schrager, 1979, p. 29) a more useful approach may be to conceptualize the problem of an LD child with NBD as one of information processing (Naylor, 1980). Within this context, variables that need to be studied are the relationships, functional or correlational, between the tonic neck reflex and attention-concentration, short and long-term visual and auditory memory and hyperactivity. It is certainly possible that persistence and magnitude of the tonic neck reflex as well as other signs of NBD contribute to the development of learning failure as a result of related problems in attention and automatized perceptual processing skills. Selection of appropriate comparison and contrast groups within the LD population that vary significantly in signs of NBD would contribute to the understanding of the contribution NBD makes to the child's failure to learn.

Study of the interrelationships between the various signs of NBD might also prove useful. The disruption in the developmental sequence where the primitive reflexes are inadequately inhibited suggest that there may be a relationship between reflex pathology and a more cognitive variable, such as the development of body image. As was noted earlier, the ATNR can be observed during the postnatal period as the child automatically assumes the "fencer position" while lying in the prone position. With the head rotated, the arm on the face side will be automatically extended, encouraging the infant to visually regard the hand on that side. During this period the tonic neck reflex domination stimulates asymmetrical visual exploration and asymmetrical development of the primary circular reactions. As the reflex becomes inhibited, symmetrical exploration is possible as the child is able to bring objects to the midline and explore them through the circular reactions. In general, the child's first exploratory approach to objects is asymmetrical, and with the inhibition of the tonic neck reflex, exploration becomes symmetrical. There is considerable observational data to support the idea that the ability for midline exploration stimulates the development of sensorimotor intelligence and that such midline behavior also contributes to the development of body image and self observation (Sherick, Greenman & Legg, 1976). For example, the normal five-month-old child constantly transfers objects from one hand to the other at midline while sitting. The proprioceptive, tactile kinesthetic, and visual sensation stimulated by transfer from one side of the body to the other, as well as systematic exploration by the circular reactions, must contribute significantly to the development of information regarding self and other objects.

The child with NBD will not have had this experience to the same degree that will be true of a normally developing child. Consequently, the former child will demonstrate basic and chronic information processing failure seen as catching a ball at midline, inadequate visual-motor coordination, as well as other problems related to midline development and body image. The measurement and manipulation of variables such as midline integration and body image have not received adequate research study with LD children with NBD. Data regarding the existence and function of such variables in this population would add to our theoretical knowledge of developmental psychology and also add to our understanding of these children.

Chapter 6

Postural Reflexes
and Equilibrium Reactions

Introduction

As the primitive reflexes become adaptively inhibited, a range of interrelated behaviors basic to body posture and equilibrium develop and mature. These reactions are innate, being found in infants independent of culture, and serve to maintain an adaptive relationship between the child's body and gravity. Their development is most clearly observed between birth and the acquisition of walking and running. For example, placing a normal 5 month old infant in the prone position and lifting it up with the hands placed at the hip and chest will elicit the prone extension posture with the head held above the horizontal plane and limbs extended. At 8 to 12 months, or whenever the infant begins to take the first steps, observation of the various interrelated reactions of legs, hips, arms and head needed to maintain the body in its new relationship to gravity, clearly illustrates the equilibrium reactions. Unfortunately, at least from the infant's perspective, if one observes these first steps for an extended period of time the infant will fall and the protective extension reactions will be observed. If the fall is forward, the head will automatically extend and the arms will be thrust forward to protect the infant from the fall. These are automatic reactions. Later in development, especially in the area of equilibrium, these reactions can be modified by being consciously observed by the child. This will occur as the child first learns to ride a bicycle or roller skate. During such times the child modifies the reactions, and they probably should be termed adjustments. Over time, as the adjustments are made to the new demands of gravity, these become automatic, unconscious, and function as reactions.

For purposes of presentation, the primitive reflexes are discussed separately, but it is apparent that primitive and postural reflexes and equilibrium reactions all contribute to maintain the characteristic orientation of the body in space with respect to gravity. Probably one of the more prevalent aspects of clinical folklore is that many LD children are awkward or "klutsey." In what follows, data will be presented to support this clinical observation, at least for that NBD subsample of the LD population. Postural control and equilibrium reactions appear to be developed in this group to a lesser degree than that found in normal children. As a consequence, these children have never adequately adapted to the effects of gravity. This lack of adaptation in itself could contribute directly to the learning disability or more indirectly through related problems in attention-concentration and hyperactivity. However, problems in postural reflexes and equilibrium reactions may be part of a broader dysfunction in the vestibular-proprioceptive system. Another commonly assessed indicator of a dysfunction in this system is ocular-motor control and nystagmus duration. These vestibular functions will be presented independently for discussion although it is recognized that there is a risk of losing the child in a maze of independent discussions of reflexes, reactions, and adjustments.

Postural Control

A great deal of our knowledge regarding the neurophysiological basis of postural control is based on research with animals. The procedures used to elicit and describe the reactions in animals illustrate some of the problems in using similar procedures in the clinical evaluations of a typical latency-aged child. The basic procedure requires that the total body be manipulated in space so that the reactions of the limbs and particularly the head can be observed as indicators of the postural reflexes. In the initial studies of the tonic labyrinthine, various species of animals were manipulated in space by the experimenter and the reactions systematically recorded (Magnus, 1926). The data suggested the importance of the eyes and vision in the maintenance of adequate labyrinthine reactions. Rabbits and guinea pigs apparently do not use the optic system and consequently do not raise their heads while cats, dogs, and monkeys demonstrate the righting reactions when vision can be used but fail to do so when vision is not possible. Through a series of systematic studies of the labyrinthine reactions, it was concluded that (1) the reactions are not evoked by movement but rather by position relative to the horizontal plane, (2) the reactions depend on visual reflexes modulated by the brain stem centers, (3) generally righting reactions for head position are a function of labyrinthine, optic and tactile stimuli, while optical righting is a function of cortical centers.

It is probably because infants can be manipulated in space that the evaluation of the tonic labyrinthine reflex is frequently used in pediatric evaluations (Capute et al., 1978, p. 51-53). The problem in evaluating the tonic labyrinthine reflex in LD children is that by the time a child of average intelligence consistently fails to perform on academic tasks at the level expected, the child is either at the end of first grade or frequently in the second or third grade. The basic method for demonstrating the righting reactions is the systematic manipulation of the body relative to the horizontal plane and this becomes a major issue with the average child of age seven or eight. The quantitative evaluation of the reaction prior to this time is probably possible although no systematic research has been reported.

Clinical experience indicates that more accurate evaluation of the reaction can be obtained by separate scoring procedures for the reaction of the limbs and head (Pothier et al., 1983). The child is lifted in the prone position by the examiner. The evaluation of all the righting reactions require that the examiner be close to the floor and in position to lift the child comfortably for a 3 second interval. In this age range the prone extension posture is the expected reaction as illustrated in Figure 5. Increase in flexor tone in either arms, legs, and hips during this interval is the scoring criterion. No change is scored a 0; observable increase is scored 1, moderate 2, and extreme increase scored 3. The child illustrated in Figure 6 is demonstrating a moderate tonic labyrinthine reflex. In optical righting and labyrinthine righting the same procedure is used except the child is lifted in the prone and dorsal position and on each side. The scoring criteria is the position of the head relative to the horizontal plane. Head position maintained above the horizontal line of the body is scored 0, and slightly below the line is scored 1. If the head drops below the line of the body during the 3 second interval, a score of 2 is given, and if the child does not raise the head during the interval, a score of 3 is given. In the assessment of labyrinthine righting, the child's eyes are covered with a soft comfortable cloth. Obviously there are a number of features of this evaluation that create problems. The most obvious is the child's reaction to being manipulated in space by a relative stranger and the use of a blindfold. Clinical observation indicated that the righting reactions could not be reliably assessed in older children and consequently it is recommended only to be used with chil-

65

Figure 5: Prone Extension Posture. Head, shoulders, arms, and legs reacting against the pull of gravity.

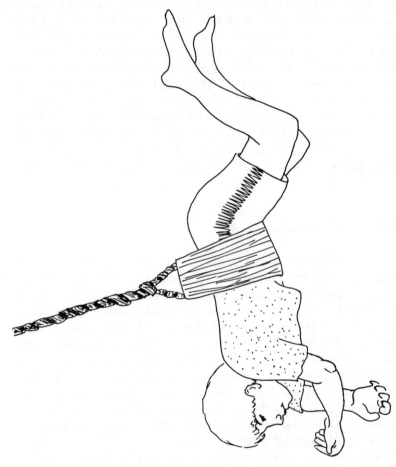

Figure 6: Tonic Labyrinthine Reflex. Increase in Flexor tone as head, shoulders, arms and legs react with the pull of gravity.

dren six years old or less who can be appropriately manipulated by the examiner. Evaluation of the tonic labyrinthine reflex and prone extension posture is an area in which more systematic efforts at developing a reliable and valid assessment procedure are needed. The basic problem is to develop an assessment technique for LD children that has clinical utility and produces meaningful data for research purposes. There have been recent efforts to develop an objective procedure for evaluating the prone extension posture that is suitable for children ages 4 through 8 (Gregory-Flock & Yerxa, 1984). The evaluation procedures from the PRPA need more research with a younger population. Evaluation of the tonic labyrinthine reflex in children below age six, which is probably possible with the PRPA, might be useful for identifying and studying children at-risk for learning disabilites. However, this would add little to our knowledge regarding the occurrence of dysfunctional reactions in a clearly identified LD sample.

Equilibrium Reactions

Pathological conditions in the vestibular system have a long history of being evaluated by equilibrium reactions in adults (Kornhuber, 1974) and infants (Capute et al., 1978). Inadequate static balance or balance during movement can be a symptom of a variety of vestibular diseases such as Menieres. It should be clear that the evaluation of equilibrium problems to be discussed here is only appropriate in the context where adequate medical examination indicates no medical diagnosis or treatment. In infants, equilibrium reactions are often referred to as tilting reactions. The basic procedures used to assess equilibrium in infants is very similar to that used to evaluate LD children and consists in systematically varying the child's relationship to gravity to record the body's compensating reactions. The integrity of the vestibular system is evaluated by systematically stressing that system. In terms of neurophysiology, vestibular functions are interrelated with proprioception and the cerebellum, and a more thorough evaluation of the integrity of these systems is not necessary for the child of concern in this text. Procedures used to evaluate the vestibular system in LD children are directly related to its anatomy and physiology. The vestibular nuclei, located in the brain stem, functions to both inhibit and facilitate muscle tone and influence muscle activity involved in postural movements and equilbrium. The nonauditory

68

organ of the inner ear consists of the vestibular apparatus that has a close relationship with the brain stem vestibular nuclei in maintaining adequate body posture, equilibrium, and spatial orientation. The utricle, saccule, and semicircular canals form the vestibular apparatus. Impulses originating in the utricle and saccule are conducted by the vestibular nerve to control the organism's response to gravitational forces in either the static-state or during movement, as well as direction of eye gaze, and maintenance of plane of vision dependent on position of head. These various functions are dependent on the ampulla of the semicircular canals and the maculae of the utricle and saccule. The receptor organs are sensitive to stimulation produced by rotary or turning movement and gravitational changes due to linear acceleration, head position in space, and body orientation (Nobak & Demarest, 1975).

The vestibular system contributes to the development of postural reactions, such as the tonic labyrinthine reflex, discussed earlier, and plays a similar role in the equilibrium reactions. Pronounced forms of vestibular pathology in children with CNS involvement is observed in cerebral palsy where postural rigidity and instability, falling, imbalance and tonus abnormalities occur (Bobath, 1963). In infancy vestibular integrity is evaluated by the occurrence of a sequence in the development of protective equilibrium reactions (Milani-Comparetti & Gidoni, 1967). The initial occurrence of protective reactions is elicited by a sudden displacement of the erect trunk. The protective function of these reactions is seen by their spontaneous elicitation in the direction of a fall. The parachute reaction can be elicited at four months by the sudden displacement of the infant downward and spontaneous extension of the lower limbs and flexion of the upper limbs. At approximately six months, sideways protective extension of the upper limbs can be elicited and one month later forward protective extension of both arms occurs. At nine months, backward protective extension of both arms is demonstrated. The protective reactions develop in concert with motor milestones that significantly redefine the infant's relationship with gravity. The growth toward vertical orientation is also accompanied by the development of the equilibrium reactions. Protective reactions function when the law of gravity prevails whereas equilibrium reactions prevent the tendency to fall. In the pediatric evaluation of equilibrium reactions the curving of the spine is a significant indicator of development. The key reaction is the curvature of the spine in the opposite direction of the pull of gravity. The adequacy of this reaction serves to make the development of erect posture safe as well as adaptive and during the evaluation the infant is tilted in various directions and the reactions observed. At five months the infant is tilted in the prone position and in the supine at seven months. Between seven and twelve months the evaluation takes place first in the sitting position and finally in the quadruped. Curvature of the spine is a useful index in infancy, but as the child develops, the coordinated anti-gravity movements of the legs, hips, arms, shoulder and head can be used as signs of equilibrium reactions. Although somewhat different procedures are used to elicit protective extension reactions and equilibrium reactions, sudden loss of support in the former and gradual shifting of gravitational pull in the latter, conceptually the reactions are part of the human organism's total adaptation to maintaining a vertical orientation to the world.

The basic procedure used to evaluate the equilibrium reactions in infancy, systematically manipulating the relationship between the body and gravity, has been used in neurology to clinically evaluate the integrity of the vestibular system. For example, in the Rombergs test the individual is in the standing position with both feet together, upper limbs hanging to the side of the body and eyes closed. A variation of this procedure includes having the individual stand on one leg and testing with eyes open and closed. These procedures have been applied in the evaluation of LD children (Ayres, 1980; deQuiros & Schrager, 1979). One of the major indicators of dysfunction is the tendency to fall, with the direction of the fall suggesting the area of CNS pathology. Other signs include unusual separation between the feet, greater withdrawal of one arm from the axis of the body, and associated movements such as opening the mouth and clenching and opening the fingers. In general, these procedures, although used a great deal in clinical practice, have not been subject to evaluation by research. There is a great deal of room for interpretation in terms of which particular reaction is deviant from the norm, but more importantly, which pattern of reactions is deviant. For example, the syndrome of vestibular-proprioceptive dissociation is clinically diagnosed by the dominance of proprioception on one side of the body and vestibular action on the opposite side (deQuiros & Schrager, 1979, p. 189). When tested in the one leg position, the major reactions are a displacement of the body weight toward the supporting leg while the upper limbs on that side may abduct or be held close to the side. The limbs on the opposite side are held firmly against the body to produce proprioceptive and tactual feedback. This syndrome of vestibular dysfunction is discriminate from vestibular-ocularmotor split by clinically unexpected nystagmus reactions (deQuiros & Schrager, 1979, p. 192). Although the importance of making a differential diagnosis between these two syndromes is stressed, no research data is provided to support their existence. However, they are well described behaviorally, and it should be possible to evaluate them objectively. There is evidence that assessing children between the ages of 4 and 8 for equilibrium reactions with the eyes closed and balanced on one foot produces unreliable data (Ayres 1980, Table 80).

Attempts to objectively assess equilibrium reactions have been made as part of a general evaluation of motor proficiency (Bruininks, 1977) and a general evaluation of primitive reflexes, postural control and equilibrium reactions (Pothier et al., 1983). For the evaluation of motor proficiency, equilibrium is evaluated while the child is stationary and moving, and is evaluated on the PRPA with the child in various stationary positions while gravity is systematically manipulated. The procedures used in the PRPA are similar to those used in pediatric evaluations but modified for objective scoring and to be appropriate for an older age range of children. Equilibrium reactions are assessed on a 1.2 x 1.2 meter carpeted platform, 3.5 centimeters thick, that is centered on a fulcrum that is 1.2 meters long. When assessed, the child is always placed in the middle of the platform and equilibrium reactions observed in three positions: quadruped, sitting and standing. If needed, the child may also be evaluated in the dorsal position. In each position the child is tilted eight times with the fulcrum to the side and an equal number of times with the fulcrum to the midline. Scores of the total equilibrium reaction assessment can range from 0, indicating adequate reactions, to 12, indicating significant dysfunctions. In general, adequate reactions are observed when the head and/or trunk deviate to the oppostive side of the tilt, while the arms flexibly abduct and extend in a coordinated manner. A score of 1 is obtained when head and/or trunk do not deviate to the opposite side and the limbs are rigid or limp, yet balance is maintained. At any point where balance is not maintained as evidenced by movement of the feet, a score of 2 is obtained.

When balance is not maintained it is possible to observe protective extension but difficult to score because of the child's position. Protective extension is scored independently of the equilibrium reactions, although it is considered an integral part of the child's adaptation to gravity. To evaluate protective extension, the examiner grasps the child at the hips from behind. The child's arms should be hanging loosely to the side and the examiner tells the child that s/he will be

71

lifted. The examiner lifts and tilts the child forward so that the head cannot hit the floor. Immediate extension of arms and hands adequate to protect the head is scored a 0. If the extension of the arms and hands to protect the head is slow but present, the reaction is scored one. A score of two is given if arms and hands are too slow and/or inefficient to protect the head. Like postural control, children too heavy or tall should not be evaluated for protective extension using this procedure.

Equilibrium Reactions in LD Children

Problems in equilibrium reactions have often been assessed as part of a more general evaluation of motor problems in LD children. The data indicates that LD children demonstrate inadequate equilbrium reactions when compared to appropriate contrast groups. In a comparison of eleven LD males with an equal number of males making academic progress, the LD sample consistently demonstrated more deviant motor scores (Freides et al., 1980). This was a blind evaluation done by viewing video tapes of an assessment of primitive reflexes, gross motor activities and equilibrium reactions. Equilibrium reactions were assessed by a tilt board procedure and proved to be one of the more sensitive indicators of dysfunctions discriminating between the two groups. Although the LD sample consistently scored in the more deviant direction in this study, the sample size was small and the interscorer reliability of 35 items of the 97 item evaluation procedure was not satisfactory. The authors do not mention what these 35 items were.

In another study of overall motor proficiency, significant differences between a larger sample of LD children and children demonstrating no academic problems were established (Bruininks & Bruininks, 1977). This was a well designed investigation of 55 children whose academic achievement was more than a grade and one half below predicted grade level in early primary grades and two or more grades below predicted grade level in the upper elementary grades. These children were compared with an equal number of contrast children on a well standardized scale evaluating running speed and agility, bilateral coordination, strength, upper limb coordination, response speed, visual motor control, upper limb speed and dexterity, as well as equilibrium in a stationary position and in the act of movement (Bruininks, 1977). Test-retest correlations for the subtests

72

ranged from .70 to .90 and the coefficients for total and composite scores were in the .80s. Statistical analysis demonstrated an interaction effect with older children showing more motor proficiency than younger children. The LD sample demonstrated a lower total score than did the contrast group and analysis of subtest scores established that the LD children scored significantly lower on equilibrium reactions as well as other subtests.

The PRPA procedure for evaluating equilibrium reactions was used to evaluate the sample of normal, mentally retarded and LD children described earlier (Morrison, 1982). In the PRPA scoring system, the scores from the evaluation of both equilibrium and protective extension reactions are used as an indicator of adaptive reactions. Interscorer reliability for equilibrium reactions in the normal sample was .79 (p = .001), for the mentally retarded children it was .85 (p > .001) and for the LD children it was .95 (p > .001). Comparison between the three groups using MANOVA procedures established a group effect, and analysis of the equilibrium reactions demonstrated that the LD children often scored in the more dysfunctional direction than did either the mentally retarded or normal children. For example, when evaluated in the sitting position the LD children scored significantly higher than did either of the other two groups. The LD children also demonstrated more inadequate protective extension than the other two groups whose scores did not differ significantly. When assessed in the standing position, the LD and mentally retarded children showed equal difficulty in maintaining balance and more so than did the normal children. That the PRPA evaluation is measuring deviant development is indicated by the fact that of the six equilibrium assessments discriminating between the three groups, the normal sample scored lower on all of them than did the LD and the mentally retarded children.

Conclusion

The evidence reviewed so far supports the conclusion that some children having significant academic problems also demonstrate neurobehavioral dysfunctions as evidenced by inadequate inhibition of primitive reflexes and inadequate equilibrium reactions. That these same children may have significant problems in postural control is suggested by clinical observation, but inadequate evaluation procedures for quantitative study has hampered research efforts in this area. The abnormalities in primitive reflexes and equilibrium reactions are part of the signs considered indicative of vestibular processing dysfunction and support a more medically oriented approach to evaluation of learning disabilities (deQuiros & Schrager, 1979). However, various educators have stressed perceptual-motor functions in both educational assessment and intervention. Kephart (1960) in particular emphasizes the role of adequate equilibrium in the establishment of what he termed the child's perceptual-motor world. In development, extension and combination of motor patterns lead to motor generalizations resulting in the integration and incorporation of motor patterns into broader motor skills that have a direct relationship to a similar generalization in the child's intellectual development. Basic to adaptive motor generalization are adaptive responses to gravity. Remedial activities recommended by Kephart, such as walking the balance beam and using the trampoline, are important for educational purposes because adequate responses to these activities which stress the child's reactions to gravity, contribute to motor generalizations and academic achievement.

Whether or not intervention for problems in equilibrium reactions are related to academic problems, Kephart's observation of the problems these children have in their adaptation to gravity has received research support. A more general dysfunction of the vestibular system is suggested by clinical and research studies of ocular-motor control and nystagmus in LD samples (Ayres, 1978, deQuiros, 1976, Frank & Levinson, 1976). These studies have stimulated research indicating that inadequate equilibrium reactions are accompanied by deviant vestibular-ocular reflexes in a number of LD children. Considering the vestibular system as an information processing system suggests that any dysfunction in the system would result in inadequate sensory-perceptual data. In a sense, what Kephart refers to as dysfunctions in the child's perceptual-motor world might be more precisely described and investigated as dysfunctions in information processing. This may be particularly true in conceptualizing the contribution made by vestibular and ocular-motor dysfunctions to the acquisition of reading decoding and comprehension skills. Dysfunctions in information processing are evidenced in inadequacies in attention-concentration, hyperactivity, visual-sequencing problems and insufficient short and long term memory for visually presented data. All these processes could be negatively affected by persistent tonic neck reflexes and poor body image, inadequate adaptation to gravity and inadequate ocular-motor control.

Chapter 7

Ocular-Motor Control
and the Vestibular System

Introduction

One of the major characteristics of children is that they are frequently in motion. Adaptive inhibition of primitive reflexes and development of postural and equilibrium reactions play a major role in ambulation, but movement of any kind requires a major accommodation in ocular-motor responses. Anatomically and physiologically, posture and equilibrium reaction and ocular-motor responses are major functions of the vestibular system. There are a variety of ocular-motor responses that have been studied with learning disabled children, but this chapter will deal primarily with those ocular responses that function to maintain a constant visual image in situations where the child is moving and the object to be observed is stationary; the child is stationary and the object is moving; or any combination of these events. Maintaining a constant image under such circumstances is a complex adaptive process, but a major aspect of the process is the automatic compensatory movements of the eyes termed nystagmus. Nystagmus itself is a complex process, and various methods have been used to measure and describe it. Physiological nystagmus is the 30-70 cycles of oscillation per second in the slow movement of the eye over an observed object. There is evidence that the oscillation and change in position serve to maintain a constant visual image by preventing nerve fatigue. A different type of nystagmus can be observed in infants in the "doll's eyes reflex." To elicit this reflex the infant is held upright and tilted back. Nystagmus is observed as the eyes roll in the opposite direction to maintain the original spatial orientation. Recently, a number of investigators have developed techniques to evaluate the integrity of the infant's vestibular system by rotary stimulation to produce nystagmus (Tibbling, 1969). Nystagmus produced by rotation is observed by continued back and forth horizontal movement of the eyeballs when rotation is stopped. Normative data has been acquired and there are indications that both deviations above or below the mean nystagmus duration time for normal infants are found in infants at-risk (DeGangi, 1982). In general, unlike the primitive reflexes and equilibrium reactions, nystagmus has not been evaluated in routine pediatric examinations. This is probably due to the fact that commonly used procedures to stress the vestibular system, and to elicit nystagmus, require rotating the infant rapidly or irrigating the ear with water. Either one of these procedures would probably elicit several other reflexes in the infant, such as the crying reflex, which would make objective quantified evaluation difficult.

An example of the function of nystagmus during reading can be observed by the reader holding this page in front of his or her eyes and looking at a line of words. Neither turning the head back and forth, about three times per second, nor moving the page back and forth at the same rate, will impair the reader's ability to read the words printed on the page. The optokinetic reflex is demonstrated when the page moves and the head remains still, while the vestibular-ocular reflex is elicited when the page is held still and the head moves. In the latter situation the reader may have been aware of various kinesthetic cues, especially from the neck and head, that were being produced at the same time as the vestibular-ocular reflex. These cues contribute significantly to the adaptations that must be made to obtain consistent visual information when the human organism and environment interact through motion. The importance of an adequately functioning vestibular system for reading can be appreciated when it is necessary for a child to read signs on a freeway from a moving car, or the license plate number of a car moving past a stationary or moving child. Reading from a text requires a number of interdependent head and eye movements, some a function of the vestibular system while others are a function of related systems such as the optic. The details of the relationship between the vestibular-optic system are not well known but obviously the two must interact during reading acquisition and acquired reading. For example, as the stationary child reads a text, especially during the acquisition phase of reading, the eyes and the head move from left to right and down the page. This process involves both vestibular and optic systems.

Eye movements can be measured in a variety of ways other than nystagmus, such as vergence, miniature eye movements, flicks intraocular movements and saccades. There is a considerable amount of research investigating the relationship between these responses and reading retardation. As is true of a great deal of research in learning disabilities, the results of some studies indicate that there is no relationship between ocular-motor functions and reading retardation, while other studies indicate that there is a relationship. These studies of eye movements and reading have received adequate and recent reviews (Leisman, 1975, Pavlidis, 1981) and will not be addressed here. There are a limited number of systematic studies investigating the possible relationship between nystagmus, other ocular-motor responses and reading retardation. Frank and Levinson (1976) claim to have established a functional relationship between optokinetic nystagmus and reading retardation through analyses of their "blurring speed" data. However, their published results are difficult to interpret because of inadequate sample description, definition of reading retardation, and data analysis. As part of a syndrome of vestibular processing dysfunction, other clinicians (Ayres, 1978; deQuiros, 1976) have noted significant variations in nystagmus duration as characteristic of a number of LD children. Research into the relationship between vestibular dysfunction and learning disabilities has been advanced by the development of a postrotary method for evaluating vestibular-ocular nystagmus in children and the development of norms for nystagmus duration elicited by the procedure. The discussion to follow will focus on these developments as they have contributed to research with LD children. The research strongly supports the conclusion that there is a sub-sample of children in the LD population who demonstrate extreme nystagmus reactions, as measured by duration following rotary stimulation. These results suggest that a chronic dysfunction in the non-optic reflex system may contribute to a general dysfunction in the ocular-motor responses basic to reading acquisition.

The Vestibular Apparatus and Motion

At least a cursory acquaintance with the anatomy and physiology of the vestibular apparatus is necessary to understand the use of some of the evaluative procedures to be described. The major functions of the vestibular system are facilitated by the end organs of the inner ear and the vestibular tracts and nuclei. The vestibular apparatus of the inner ear consists of the semicircular canals, the utricle, and the saccule. The three canals are located in the labyrinth, which is embedded in the temporal bone. These canals, the posterior, superior, and lateral, or horizontal, are connected to the utricle at one end and at the other end bulge into the ampulla. When in the upright position relative to gravity the anterior and posterior canals are vertical and at right angles to each other. Relative to these two canals the lateral canal is perpendicular and horizontal. An endolymph fluid is contained in the canals, and cristae, hairlike cells in the ampulla, project into the cupula which is a gelatinous flap. The response of these structures to motion is observed when the head is accelerated at an angle. Under this condition the endolymph fluid in the plane of the semicircular canal remains stationary as the cupula rotates in the direction of acceleration while the cristae in the cupula are deflected in the direction opposite of rotation. The otolith receptor consists of the utricle and the saccule which also have hair-like cells called maculae and are also filled with endolymph. When the head is vertical, the maculae are horizontal in the utricle and vertical in the saccule. The maculae have loosely attached calcium carbonate crystals, called otoconia, which function to resist the occurrence of external forces. During linear acceleration, the crystals in the utricle and saccule remain stable while the macula deflect backward (Nobak & Demarest, 1975).

The sense organs of the utricle and saccule are the maculae and the otoconia. The maculae serve as information sources to the vestibular nuclei of the brain. The otoliths are sensitive to both the magnitude and direction of linear acceleration and the effects of gravity. There is data to indicate that the otoliths contribute to the position of the head, eye movements, and to the organism's response to vibration (Parker, 1980). Angular acceleration and deceleration are monitored by the semicircular canals functioning in pairs, with acceleration resulting in excitation in one member of a pair of bilateral canals and inhibition in the other (Kornhuber, 1974). A number of pathological conditions of the vestibular apparatus are known to cause disturbances in motion and balance (Spector, 1967). Hypoactive vestibular responses can indicate degeneration of the inner ear due to chronic inflammation or diffuse labyrinthitis. Patients with damage to a vestibular root, vestibular neuronitis, or a fracture of the petrous bone will be hyporesponsive. Abnormalities in nystagmus are often observed in patient's with a vestibular disturbance and are used diagnostically. For example, spontaneous nystagmus may be caused from a peripheral lesion of the labyrinthine structures. The eye movement may be of mixed direction but predominantly horizontal with some rotary and/or vertical components.

In previous discussion it was noted that the vestibular apparatus is basic to reflex mechanisms for posture and equilibrium and has a close anatomical and physiological relationship with the optic system. In terms of motion, besides nystagmus, the vestibular apparatus contributes to (1) the saccadic movements of the eyes when the organism is stable or in motion, (2) provides information to the organism regarding self-motion and spatial orientation during motion, (3) facilitates and integrates information for coordinated muscle control, and (4) integrates information regarding body movement and eye movement. These are all automatic functions that develop into stable adaptive responses by the second year of life.

The Measurement of Nystagmus

Nystagmus movements are categorized as vertical, oblique, horizontal, or rotary depending on the plane in which the movements occur. There are three basic measures of these movements: frequency, amplitude, and duration. Frequency is the measure of eyeball oscillations per unit of time and amplitude is the distance of each excursion of the eye. Duration, which has been used as a dependent variable in much of the research with LD children, is the length of time that nystagmus persists. Nystagmus may be measured by unaided observation or by electronystagmography (ENG). The ENG is a function of an electrical change of corneal-retinal potential and the change in electrical charge when the ocular globe moves (Keating, 1979).

The vestibular-ocular reflex, as measured by duration of postrotary nystagmus, has received the most systematic study with LD children. However, there are other methods for producing nystagmus that could be used with this population. Although it has not been researched extensively with LD children, the optokinetic reflex has been studied in medical research and can be evaluated by procedures that are sound enough to produce reliable data.

Optokinetic Nystagmus

This reflex is elicited when a stationary subject observes a succession of moving objects. Methods for clinical evaluation of the optokinetic nystagmus were first developed by Barany in 1906. Barany was a Viennese physician who was interested in the clinical significance of nystagmus demonstrated by both the optokinetic reflex and the postrotary reflex. In current clinical practice the optokinetic reflex can be evaluated by two similar procedures (Dix, 1980). One procedure has the subject seated in front of a small rotating drum. The drum consists of a cylinder, 30 cm in diameter, with black perpendicular stripes. The drum can be fixed in various positions relative to the plane of reflex to be elicited. Left or right rotation is possible and speed of rotation is controlled at three levels: 72° per second, 180° per second, and 360° per second. Subjects are instructed to look at the upper part of the drum, allowing an observer a better view of eye movements. Subjects are also asked to count the stripes as they rotate. This prevents them from staring through the drum which may inhibit nystagmus. The use of the small drum demands the co-operation of the subject and the field of vision tested is limited. As an alternative procedure the subject is seated in the center of a large rotating drum which encompasses the total visual field. The large drum procedure has certain practical disadvantages, but has the major advantage that it is practically impossible for the subject to inhibit the reflex under the stimulus condition.

A variation of these two procedures is the blurring speed test which has been developed for children with reading retardation (Frank & Levinson, 1976). There are three methods of presentation. The subject is seated before a foreground on which (1) black lettered words and phrases are systematically rotated across a blank neutral background at various speeds, (2) the same letters and phrases are rotated at various speeds against a scenic background, and (3) the foreground remains stationary while the scenic background is set in motion. In the first two procedures the subject reports at what speed blurring is perceived and this data is recorded, while in the third procedure the speed interval in which the presence or absence of foreground movement and/or blurring occurs is recorded. The particular value of these three procedures for evaluating nystagmus in LD children is not made clear and the blurring speed test requires considerable more research before its reliability and parameters of validity are established.

Vestibular-Ocular Reflex

There are several different procedures available to evaluate this reflex. The sinusodial acceleration procedure (Mathog, 1972) has not been used in research with LD children while caloric stimulation has been used extensively in assessing LD children (deQuiros & Schrager,

1978). In this procedure, warm or cold water is used as a stimulant against the tympanic membrane to elicit the vestibular-ocular reflex. One of the major limitations of this procedure is that although it has been used extensively in the evaluation of vestibular dysfunctions in LD children, and children at-risk for learning disabilities, there is inadequate normative data on children available at this time. There are indications that there are age effects, with younger subjects demonstrating low frequency repetitions and large excursions, and older subjects demonstrating high frequency repetitions and short excursions (Van der Laan & Oosterweld, 1974). The judgement as to which variation in nystagmus is considered deviant or within the normal range is based on clinical experience rather than reference to established norms. Although this may be adequate for clinical practice, it is a major limitation to the use of caloric stimulation for research purposes.

The integrity of the vestibular system through the examination of the vestibular-ocular reflex can be accomplished by rotary stimulation. This procedure has been standardized for children with the Southern California Postrotary Nystagmus Test (PNT) developed by Ayres (1975). Normative data for children between the ages of 3 to 10 is available (Ayres, 1975; Kimball, 1981; Punwar, 1982). The procedures used in the PNT are similar to those developed by Barany in the early 1900s. In the basic procedure the child sits cross-legged on a platform equipped with ball-bearing wheels. The child grips the edge of the platform with the head flexed at a 30° angle. The environment should not have windows or objects for fixation. The platform is rotated at constant speed ten times in 20 seconds, and the examiner estimates the duration of nystagmus beginning immediately after rotation is stopped. The child is rotated to the left and to the right. Duration estimates are made for each direction and may be summed for the total duration time. The child is instructed to look forward, preferably at a blank, neutral colored surface, after rotation cessation. Although the ENG can be used to record nystagmus, the existing data has been established by examiners observing the duration of nystagmus. Both duration and excursion of nystagmus can be measured with the PNT. However, duration has been used almost exclusively in the clinical research literature.

Stability of Postrotary Nystagmus Duration

Factors affecting postrotary nystagmus are numerous (Royeen, 1980). This is to be expected since the vestibular system is known to be sensitive and adaptive to stimulus change. When a subject is repeatedly rotated in one direction the reflex will decrease in the direction of rotation. Adaptation is also a function of factors such as darkness and fixation. Repeated rotation in darkness will result in some reduction in the slow phase of the reflex, but significantly less reduction than is true of rotation in lighted conditions. Suppression of nystagmus and dizziness following rotation is possible by visual fixation on an object during rotation, a technique used by ballet dancers. Nystagmus following rotation can also be reduced by manipulation of the mental state of the subject. Using verbal instruction to manipulate state and measuring nystagmus by ENG, Montgomery and Capps (1980) demonstrated reduced duration in children under reverie conditions. Other extravestibular factors that may produce variation in nystagmus include time of testing, medications, and the subjects' participation in the evaluation (Montgomery & Rodel, 1982).

There are indications that postrotary nystagmus is affected by age or that errors in measurement of duration are affected by age. In an effort to gather data on the reliability of the PNT for three to four year-olds, 28 children in the former age range and 42 children in the latter age range were evaluated. There were no effects of age or sex reported and the total mean duration score in seconds was 18.61, SD = 4.23 for the three-year olds and 18.93, SD = 5.82, for the four year-old children. (Deitz, Siegner & Crowe, 1981). Although slightly lower, these duration scores are similar to those presented in Table 1. A later study by the same researchers (Siegner, Crowe & Deitz, 1982), using the same procedure with five-year-old children, resulted in quite different duration scores: mean = 14.00, SD = 3.84. This score is approximately one standard deviation below that obtained for the two earlier age groups and more than the standard deviation for the same age range in Table 1. Data gathered by other researchers indicates that between the ages of 3-10, sex and age do not appear to systematically affect nystagmus duration (Kimball, 1981; Punwar, 1982).

Considering the various factors that might influence duration scores, the unexplained variation in duration found in the normal five-year-old sample might be explained by difficulties in measurement and lack of reliability. However, a significant number of studies

82

Means and Standard Deviations of Duration Measurements by Groups

Age Levels by Years	3		4		5		6		7		8		9		10	
Sex	M	F	M	F	M	F	M	F	M	F	M	F	M	F	M	F
N	15	7	12	13	24	20	27	28	22	39	33	29	41	43	8	11
Mean Scores to the Left	11.13	10.28	10.33	9.46	11.04	9.20	9.92	9.64	10.85	8.72	11.0	8.86	9.95	9.07	10.12	9.45
Standard Deviation to the Left	2.32	2.43	1.67	1.19	3.23	2.16	2.65	2.99	3.05	2.12	3.13	2.76	2.28	2.65	2.41	2.54
Mean Scores to the Right	10.60	10.85	10.83	9.92	11.16	9.60	9.96	9.89	10.33	8.90	10.78	9.27	10.17	9.72	9.25	9.90
Standard Deviation to to the Right	2.26	1.77	1.80	1.44	3.06	2.70	2.73	2.55	2.97	2.87	3.30	2.10	2.41	2.75	2.05	2.66
Mean Scores, Total Duration	21.73	21.14	21.16	19.38	22.20	18.80	19.88	19.53	21.19	17.62	21.78	18.13	20.12	18.79	19.37	19.36
Standard Deviation Total Duration	4.16	4.01	2.72	1.85	5.83	4.54	5.01	5.12	5.65	4.64	5.79	4.68	4.28	4.91	4.17	4.73
(Punwar, 1982)																

From the *American Journal of Occupational Therapy*, Vol. 36, Issue 3, Page 185, Table 1. Reprinted with the permission of the American Occupational Therapy Association Inc. Copyright 1982.

have reported satisfactory reliability estimates for duration scores obtained by observation using the PNT. Using the total duration score as an indicator of stability, repeated evaluation by the same examiner over a six-week interval of 69 children produced reliability estimates of r = .62 for a three-year-old sample and r = .83 for four-year-olds (Deitz et al. 1981). Using procedures to minimize auditory and visual cues that might influence interobserver judgement of duration, Siegner et al. (1982) established high interscorer reliabilities for duration to the left (r = 95), and to the right (r = .89) and total duration score (r = .96). Nineteen developmentally normal five-year-old children were used as subjects. When evaluated over a two-week interval, 56 children between the ages of three to ten demonstrated stable duration scores to the left (r = .73), right (r = .79) and total duration (r = .82) (Punwar, 1982). Strong support for the reliability of nystagmus duration obtained by the PNT, is provided by Kimball (1981) who retested 63 children 2 1/2 years after an initial evaluation and found a significant relationship for total duration (r = .80). In general, nystagmus duration in normal children estimated by observation has produced reliable interobserver and test-retest estimates that are satisfactory for clinical and research purposes. There is also data indicating that nystagmus measured by observation is as accurate as that obtained by ENG (Keating, 1979).

Nystagmus in LD Children

As subjects participating in the PNT procedure, LD children may exhibit various behaviors that could produce variability in duration scores. Although hyponystagmus and hypernystagmus are thought to be characteristic of LD children with vestibular dysfunction, this is based on clinical observation and not on systematic research. There are reasons to believe that reliable nystagmus duration scores may be more difficult to obtain in LD children than is the case with developmentally normal children. There appears to be an interactive pattern in LD children in which vestibular processing dysfunction with hyponystagmus, and behaviors such as restlessness, distractibility, and inappropriate social interaction are common (Ottenbacher, Watson & Short, 1979). These behaviors could certainly influence the outcome of the evaluative data. Finally, problems in postural insecurity related to difficulties in balance could influence the child's ability to maintain a stable position both during and at cessation of rotation and thereby make accurate reading of duration a problem.

84

To address these issues of the reliability and the distribution of nystagmus duration scores in this population, 89 LD children with an
average age of 8 years, 2 months were evaluated with the PNT
(Morrison & Sublett, 1983). The intellectual level and academic
achievement of these children are summarized in Table 2. These children had average intelligence but were performing below grade level
in spelling, arithmetic, reading decoding and comprehension. Intra-
scorer reliability was established with 52 children using the same
examiner with a 20 minute interval between testing. The first evaluation was completed with the total sample, but during the second
assessment 37 children were either unwilling or unable to be evaluated again. Interscorer reliability was established by having two different examiners independently and simultaneously score for nystagmus duration (Morrison, 1985). This procedure included 41 children
from the total sample. Short term stability of duration for the total
sample was examined by having different examiners retest individual
children 1-4 weeks after the first evaluation. The results of the three
evaluations are summarized in Table 3.

Table 2: Intellectual Level and Academic Achievement of Learning
Disabled Sample. WISC-R and WRAT Standard Scores and
Gates-MacGinitie Normal Curve Equivalent Scores

	LD Sample		Developmentally Normal	
	Mean	SD	Mean	SD
WISC-R (Short Form)				
Intelligence	102.5	16.7	100	15
WRAT				
Spelling	88.5	12.8	100	15
Arithmetic	91.6	11.9	100	15
Reading Decoding	92.2	12.3	100	15
Gates MacGinitie				
Reading Comprehension	25.8	17.7	50	21

Table 3: Results of Three Repeated PNT Evaluations of a Learning Disabled Sample of Children

Evaluation	Mean Duration	SD
First (N = 89)		
Left	7.03	4.96
Right	6.93	4.45
Total	14.13	8.64
Twenty Minute Interval		
Second (N = 52)		
Left	6.50	5.04
Right	6.67	4.06
Total	13.11	8.39
One to Four Week Interval		
Third (N = 89)		
Left	6.44	4.28
Right	6.42	4.26
Total	12.72	7.50

Mean scores and standard deviations remained essentially the same over the time of the evaluations. Intrascorer reliability for rotation to the left was $r = .57$, ($p = .000$), to the right $r = .59$ ($p = .000$), and for the total score $r = .67$ ($p = .000$). Procedures to examine the interscorer reliability resulted in reliability estimates of $r = .84$ for duration following both left and right rotations. Short-term test retest reliabilities were, $r = .52$ ($p = .000$) for rotation to left, $r = .61$ for rotation to the right, and $r = .72$ ($p = .000$) for the total duration score. Long term stability estimates for the total duration score were available for 37 children from this sample (Morrison, 1985). These children remained in their special class program for 9 months between the two evaluations. The two evaluations were completed by different examiners and produced a reliability estimate of $r = .66$ ($p < .001$) for the total duration score.

Examination of Table 3 and the data available from Punwar's normative study with the PNT summarized in Table 1 suggest that the mean and standard deviation of this sample of LD children may be different from developmentally normal children. Using the data from the third evaluation in Table 3 and the data for developmentally normal eight-year-old boys in Table 1, the variance and means of the two samples were compared (Morrison & Sublett, 1983). The LD sample demonstrated significantly greater variance to the left (F = 1.82, df = 32/88, p < .05), to the right (F = 1.66, df = 32/88, p = .05) and total variance (F = 1.67, df = 32/88, p = .05). Three t-tests adjusted for populations with unequal variance established that the LD sample had a significantly lower mean score (p < .05) for duration measures to the left, right, and total.

Conclusion

As has been found in the development of primitive reflexes, postural control and equilibrium reactions, LD children also demonstrate abnormalities in nystagmus, indicating some dysfunction in the vestibular system. Although these findings are suggestive, the issues regarding pathology in the vestibular system are extremely complex (Kornhuber, 1974). Variation in nystagmus is indicative of a variety of neuropathological conditions and it would be naive to assume that an underlying neurological cause can be isolated at this time for the effects observed in LD children. Moreover, a syndrome must be supported by behavioral as well as neurological data and there is no data at this time to indicate that the behaviors observed consistently appear in stable clusters over an extended period of time. Finally, more data is needed to establish a functional relationship between deviations in reflex and equilibrium development, ocular-motor control, and learning disabilities.

At a more immediate level, it appears that nystagmus duration as measured by the PNT has satisfactory reliability when used with developmentally normal children. There is more variation in duration in LD children and consequently reliability estimates are lower. Although variable, over time the duration scores still remained depressed, suggesting that LD children differ from developmentally normal children in both nystagmus duration and variation in duration. The fact that two different examiners can reliably estimate duration simultaneously yet over an interval of time obtain less reliable scores, suggests that the fluctuation in duration is a function of nystagmus in this sample and not examiner error. While interscorer reliability is satisfactory, the variability in duration creates some problems in obtaining a "true" estimate of an individual child's actual score and what actually constitutes hyponystagmus. In general, duration scores following rotations either to the left or right are the same and total duration scores below 13 seconds have been considered abnormally depressed. However, analysis of scores from an LD sample over a period of time indicate that a significant number of children can switch from being classified from depressed to normal nystagmus duration, and vice versa, with repeated evaluation (Morrison & Sublett, 1983). Considering variation in duration, as well as an average duration score obtained from several evaluations may be more useful in establishing what constitutes a deviant nystagmus reflex following rotation. Finally, some research has indicated that hypernystagmus may also be found in LD children (Ottenbacher, 1980). Systematic study of children consistently demonstrating this deviation in nystagmus is also needed.

Chapter 8

Movement, Visual Perception, and Bilateral Integration

Introduction

In review, the previous discussions indicate that there are a number of LD children who demonstrate subtle, but stable signs of NBD that have discriminant validity. These signs do not have a strong relationship with age, in that hyponystagmus does not change and equilibrium reactions do not improve over time. Primitive reflexes do appear to have some relationship with age in that in both developmentally normal and LD samples, these reflexes can be elicited to a greater degree in younger than in older children (Morrison, 1985). These are signs of dysfunction rather than delay and there is no evidence that this dysfunction is acquired either during birth or postnatally. There have been attempts to establish these signs as indicative of a vestibular processing dysfunction but there is not enough data to establish this as a discrete syndrome.

At this point the discussion will turn to procedures that have been used to evaluate the sensory and perceptual function of LD children. Again, the results of these evaluations indicate that LD children consistently differ from developmentally normal children. The data on sensory integration supports the conclusion that LD children are impaired in using their body to obtain reliable sensory information regarding their environment. The data obtained from neuropsychological evaluations indicates that some of these same children are also impaired in their ability to automatically respond to information available through auditory or visual modalities. The data suggests that LD children with NBD are generally impaired in the capacity to process and integrate sensory and perceptual information in learning acquisition and performance. The specific causal link with learning disabilities in this process is the failure to automatize perceptual processes that are basic to cognitive tasks such as writing and reading.

The research links NBD with perceptual processing dysfunctions indicating that these children have generalized problems at the sensory and perceptual level. The learning failure of NBD children can be understood in terms of the information processing requirements of learning acquisition and performance.

Sensory Integration

To a certain degree the discrimination between sensation and perception is an arbitrary one. The value of such a discrimination has been the subject of a great deal of discussion (Rosinski, 1977). The subtleties of these discussions will be simplified in what follows by a focus on the procedures used to evaluate sensory and perceptual functions. Information available in the child's world may be distorted by dysfunctional sensory systems such as hearing and vision. In LD children the issue is not a loss of hearing or vision but more subtle dysfunctions in these systems such as impairments in sequencing ability for data presented visually or auditorially or in combination. These difficulties may be related to a dysfunction in a particular sensory process, such as ocular-motor control, or a dysfunction in the integrative capacity of the child as evidenced in difficulties in visual-motor integration. As was mentioned earlier, observation and theory suggests that sensation and perception become integrated through movement. Because of this view the evaluation process often includes functions such as motor planing and visual-motor coordination. Here, the body as a modality for processing information is a focus of assessment, particularly as it is a source of kinesthetic data. The evaluation of equilibrium reactions and compensatory nystagmus reflexes described earlier are an example. This chapter will describe techniques employed to assess functions such as ocular-motor control and bilateral integration. Although it seems clear that children with NBD have problems in kinesthetic awareness, a functional relationship between such problems and learning disabilities has yet to be established. In general, research efforts to establish a link between sensory-motor variables and cognitive variables have been correlational studies that have produced modest results (Saphier, 1973). The ability to transfer perceptual data from one sensory modality to another has been demonstrated to be a reliable predictor of performance on cognitive tasks such as reading (Birch & Belmont, 1964). As the evaluation process moves from the assessment of the function of a particular sensory modality to the assessment of the integrative process, performance on perceptual tasks are the focus of evaluation. It is only recently that the perceptual-motor integration of children with NBD has been systematically evaluated. Although limited research data is available, the data demonstrates that these children have significant delays in this area.

The first studies to be discussed have evaluated sensory-perceptual functions that are basic to the processing of incoming information.

Ocular-Motor Functions

In the previous discussions of the evaluation of the integrity of the vestibular system, the various components of nystagmus received major attention. Nystagmus itself is but one component of a number of ocular-motor functions that contribute to the child's ability to process visually presented data. One frequently used criterion for learning disability is a significant discrepancy between a child's age or intelligence and performance on academic tasks such as reading. The possible causes of failure to read at the expected level are multiple but two quite different causes have received considerable research interest. Reading certainly can be looked upon as a language skill and therefore reading retardaiton is caused by a basic language dysfunction (Velluntino, 1977). The opposite view is that reading is basically a perceptual process and therefore reading retardation is caused by a dysfunction in the ocular-motor system (Pavlidis, 1981). In the former situation, children who become retarded readers do so because basic language abilities are deficient and consequently reading is not acquired. Reading activity itself would stimulate the development of adaptive ocular-motor responses, and in cases where poor readers have deviant ocular-motor responses this is due to lack of language skills rather than the deviant ocular-motor responses observed. In the opposing view, basic language skills are adequate but dysfunctions in the ocular-motor system have adverse effects on reading acquisition and performance. In this case the automatized processes necessary for adequate reading fail to develop because the necessary ocular-motor components are variable rather than stable. In these children independent measures of language skills, except for reading, indicate adequate performance, while ocular-motor responses are deviant. There is a good deal of evidence that reading retarded children differ significantly from normal readers in eye movements.

Besides the compensatory nystagmus responses elicited by the interaction between visual field and motion, other ocular-motor functions in LD children such as saccadic, pursuit movements and fixation have received considerable attention. When scanning a line of print, the eye does not move smoothly but in a series of step-like movements termed saccades. Although the initiation of the movement is voluntary, the velocity of the saccadic movement cannot be controlled and does not appear to be modified by practice. Saccades are high velocity movements that are a function of amplitude. During the actual movements visual perception is suppressed and it is during fixation that the printed word is perceived. Fixation itself can be categorized and measured by forward fixations, regressed fixations and duration of fixation. Pursuit movements are optokinetic nystagmus that occur when the head is stable and the eyes follow a moving visual target at the same speed and same direction as the target.

There is considerable research investigating the relationship between eye movements and reading but very little with LD children who have demonstrated NBD. Considering the evidence that hyponystagmus is found in this population, research on other ocular-motor responses such as visual pursuit and reading performance in these children could be useful. Previous research on ocular-motor function and reading has typically investigated a limited number of functions and used bivariate statistical techniques to establish a significant relationship with reading level. Measuring a range of ocular-motor functions and using MANOVA technique might establish a pattern or cluster of functions related to reading level. Another limitation in the previous research is that the possible influence of verbal intelligence has not been controlled. Language competency and ocular-motor functions may be covariants in that children with limited language do not read and consequently their ocular-motor functions are deviant. Recognizing these issues, Poynter, Schor, Haynes and Hirsch (1982), examined the relationship of four different ocular-motor functions to reading level in a design that controlled for the level of verbal intelligence. Ocular-motor measures included forward and regressive fixations, duration of fixation, and lag of accommodation. In a sample of fourth and sixth grade children who were not identified as learning disabled, ocular-motor functions had only a marginal association with reading level when examined independently. However, with and without controls for verbal intelligence, all four ocular-motor functions combined had significant negative relationships with level of reading. Lower reading ability was associated with less adaptive ocular-motor functions, with frequency of fixations and lag of accommodation having the strongest relationship. This was a well designed study that should be replicated with reading retarded children and the addition of a nystagmus measure, such as the PNT, as a control for the integrity of the vestibular system.

The eye movements of reading retarded children on non-reading tasks have also been studied. These studies reduce cognitive factors, such as level of language skill and content to be read, that may contribute to the variance in eye movement observed during reading. The eye movements in response to a moving target of two reading retarded groups were compared to two groups who were normal readers. One group in both the retarded reading and normal sample also demonstrated poor spatial functioning and children in these groups demonstrated less efficient eye movements on the target test than did either of the other two groups (Lesevre, 1968). There are a number of studies indicating that smooth pursuit movements of the eye to a moving target in retarded readers is interrupted by other movements, such as saccades (Bogacz, Mendilaharsu & Mendilaharsu, 1974; Pavlidis, 1981). The focus of most of the previous research on the relationship between the eye movements of a retarded reader on non-reading tasks has been on eye movements *per se*, whereas in actual experience, as a child looks at a moving target, eye movements occur in combination with head movements. The importance of coordinated eye and head movements for efficient vision suggests the possible contribution of the vestibular system in this process and also indicates the necessity of an experimental design that includes measures of both eye and head movements. Such a design is complicated by the fact that just as there are a variety of eye movements that may be important in the process, there are a number of head movements that can also be important. The designs must include multiple measures of movement and the interaction of eye and head movements.

In a study of the relationship between head and eye movements in reading retarded and normal children, three different eye-head patterns were measured in response to visual targets positioned at fixed intervals on a target board (Petri & Anderson, 1980). The patterns were: eye first, head first, or simultaneous eye and head movements. The only pattern that discriminated between the groups occurred when the target was presented at unexpected locations. In this condition normal children demonstrated the more common pattern of eye first responses while the reading retarded children demonstrated this response less frequently. When the target appeared at predictable locations there was no difference in eye-head movements for the two groups. Individual analysis of the eye movements of reading retarded children also suggested unusual eye-head movements to the target under both predicted and unexpected location conditions. These patterns included small saccadic movements, long fixations and eye movements prior to head movements. The function of ocular-motor responses, such as optokinetic nystagmus, is to stabilize the visual world under conditions such as movement that could produce visual instability. If this compensatory vestibular reaction does not function automatically than other movements such as saccades may contribute to the process. However, during the step-like saccadic movements, unlike the smooth compensatory movement, visual perception is suppressed. There is considerable evidence that reading retarded children make a number of erratic eye movements while reading, as well as to moving targets, and that these movements are related to poor performance on such tasks. Since ocular-motor responses are known to be related to the vestibular system, the addition of other measures of that system, such as head-eye movements, might clarify the important sensory-kinesthetic variables that may be contributing to the poorer performance consistently observed in reading retarded children.

Bilateral Integration

Data processed through the senses serving as information basic to the adaptation of the child may occur in various combinations related to the body and space. For example, a procedure commonly used in both pediatric exams and psychological assessment of infants, is to produce a sound such as ringing a small bell, to the left and right side of the infant. The criterion measure is the infant's turning in the direction of the unseen sound. The infant's capacity to visually pursue a slowly moving target is a common method of evaluating the integrity of visual perception. This discrimination as to the source of sensory stimulation takes place over time and is intimately related to the child's gradual awareness that there is a body midline and that there are two sides to the body. Although this awareness may be expressed verbally as a cognitive concept of middle, right and left, the initial awareness is nonverbal, and expressed in lateral and bilateral sensory and perceptual functions. The evaluation of these functions is important in terms of the integrity of the sensory and perceptual systems involved but has added significance because such integration is assumed to be basic to cognitive structures related to body awareness and spatial orientation.

Major sources of sensory data: the eyes, ears, legs, arms, and hands are symmetrically positioned around the central longitudinal axis of the body. This axis is the body midline, an extension of the midsagittal plane of the face that divides the body into two equal halves (Goody & Reinhold, 1952). This imaginary line develops through postural control, equilibrium responses, gross motor activites such as standing upright, walking, turning, and lying. Obviously, visual and auditory perception contribute to the development of spatial and temporal discriminations. These activities involve both halves of the body moving parallel to, in the opposite direction from, or in a rotary movement about the central axis. At a theoretical level, these movements contribute to the development of a cognitive body scheme that is basic to the child's spatial concepts. The child's reference point, or the ordinate, for the coordinate of space is the pull of gravity through the body midline (Kephart, 1960) that serves to differentiate objects in external space that are positioned to the left or right, above or below, in front of or behind this constant reference point (Luria, 1966). For example, after the child has developed a dynamic sense of the left and right side of the body, he or she is able to imagine this same symmetrical relationship beyond the limits of the body in space. This preoperational concept of space to the left and right is the basis for a later developing concept of rotating objects around a central axis. This cognitive capacity enables the child to imagine he is facing himself.

Like all preoperational thought (Piaget, 1954) these concepts are relatively unstable. However, they contribute to the differentiation of self from others. This can be seen when children finally grasp the concept that the right side of a person facing them is opposite their left side and vice versa. A dynamic concept of left and right may be relatively stable before a child of five can consistently verbally label his own right and left and it is not until age seven that he can make this discrimination with another person. That this is a complex perceptual-cognitive development is seen in the fact that it is not until almost ten years of age that children are able to consistently identify the left and right of objects (Barsch, 1968). Particularly during the acquisition period, perceptual cues for preoperational spatial concepts such as horizontal, vertical, center, left and right, contribute significantly to the development of writing and reading skills. During acquisition, stable spatial concepts are important and these concepts evolve from a stable body scheme and consequent ability to project images in space (Benton, 1955; Kephart, 1971). If the preoperational spatial concepts are not stable, then acquisition and finally achievement can be below the expected level.

Bilateral Integration and Learning Disabilities

Clinical observation of patients with known CNS pathology has suggested that difficulties crossing the midline was frequent in this population. Aphasic adults, when compared with normal adults, have difficulties imitating a model characterized by frequent uncrossed responses to a crossed stimulus (Head, 1955). Giving an ipsilateral response to a crossed model has been considered a sign of neuropathology for over seventy years (Head, 1912) and clinical evaluation indicates that this is a frequent problem in LD children. Evaluation procedures with this population have involved observation of ocular tracking past the midline and arm usage as well as imitation of a model of ipsilateral and contralateral hand usage. Problems in crossing the midline are considered as one sign among a number of signs indicating perceptual and motor dysfunctions. The tendency to avoid crossing the midline is often accompanied by problems in equilibrium and failure to consistently discriminate between the right and left side of the body. This failure in discrimination is accompanied by lack of motor coordination, persistence of primitive reflexes, and inadequate ocular-motor control when crossing the midline (Ayres, 1972). Research data for these clinical observations has been generated by studies of developmental age trends in midline behavior, comparison of LD samples and developmentally normal samples and studies of the relationship between body righting reactions and midline behavior in LD samples.

As has been noted previously, assessment of a deviancy in signs of NBD in children can best be done by a norm referenced criterion. Without some reference point, it is difficult to evaluate what is normal variation and what is significant deviancy. Clinical evaluation of midline behavior in children from age 4 to 8 years 11 months has been made more objective by the establishment of age trends in developmentally normal children in this age range (Cermak, Quintero

96

& Cohen, 1980). The Space Visualization Contralateral Use Test (SVCU) from the SCSIT (Ayres, 1980) was used to obtain a measure of a child's spontaneous tendency to cross the body at the child's midline. The test consists of a series of puzzles to be completed on a formboard which is placed at the child's midline, and two blocks, one placed slightly to the left and the other slightly to the right of the child. The scoring method has been devised to take into account preferred hand and provides a ratio measure of ipsilateral and contralateral hand usage. Results obtained from 150 children indicated that spontaneous midline crossing behavior increased with age but that the shared variance between the four age groups was such that a use x group interaction did not occur. There were no sex differences in the sample. The results also established that a score which had previously been evaluated as indicating problems in midline behavior for children 7 to 8 years of age is probably not a deviant score but rather an indication of increased hand preference for this age range. The original interpretation of the score did not take into account the possible effect of age. The limitation of this study is that no inter-rater reliablity or test-retest reliability was obtained. The test score is based on fairly observable behavior and inter-rater reliability is probably fairly high. However, considering the possible variation in hand use in children ages 4-6, since hand dominance may not be consistent in this age range, test-retest reliablity estimates would be desirable.

The SVCU Test was used in another study comparing midline crossing behavior in developmentally normal and LD children (Cermak & Ayres, 1984). In the normal sample there were 30 children from each of four age groups from five to eight, for a total of 120 children. Although this represents a sufficient number of children for purposes of comparison, the LD sample of 179 children was heterogeneous, poorly described, and included an even more heterogeneous group of five year-old children. Five year-old children may be deficient in pre-academic skills and be at-risk for learning disabilities. However, as has been noted previously, they simply cannot be considered as performing below expectations on academic tasks while having average intelligence: an accepted operational definition of learning disability. In this particular study this becomes an important discrimination, since of the LD sample this age range demonstrated the largest differences in mean score (7.1 points) from the normal controls and had the greatest variance (SD = 9.7) in the total sample. Statistical comparison established an effect for group and group x age interaction. Multiple comparisons at each age level established that the LD children scored more poorly than did the normal controls except at age 7. It is possible that including the age five LD children in the analysis accounted for the group effect. Although the results are suggestive of a difference between LD children and developmentally normal children on this measure, the results should be interpreted with some reserve because of the limits of the design.

Reflex Pathology and Bilateral Integration

The neck righting reflex is observed in infancy in response to rotation of the head. Sometimes referred to as log rolling, the reflex is seen in the extension of the spine and the simultaneous rotation of trunk and pelvis contingent with the rotation of the head while the infant is in the supine position. This primitive reflex is eventually inhibited and replaced by segmental rolling or body righting, in which rotation of the head or any of several body parts results in coordinated derotation of the remaining parts of the body (Capute et al., 1978, pp. 58-60; Morrison et al., 1978, pp. 125-126). The evidence of a possible relationship between primitive reflexes, voluntary motor responses, and midline behavior can be observed in the early developmental sequence of reflex elicitation and inhibition (Paine, 1964). The prone extension posture can be elicited in infants when they are lifted horizontally from the prone position and the arms, legs, head, trunk and spine automatically extend against the pull of gravity (Figure, 5). This same pattern of tonus change with extension of the spine as well as the asymmetrical tonus change elicited by the ATNR may be responsible for the initial appearance of the neck righting reflex. The functional relationship between reflexive and voluntary behavior can be observed at approximately 5 months in attempts by the supine infant to bilaterally engage objects placed to the side within view but out of reach. As the contralateral hand moves across the midline, the head turn elicits neck righting and the infant rolls from supine to prone in the direction of the visually regarded object.

Another example of the relationship between exploration, midline behavior, and early postural reflex patterns is seen in the reduction of the influence of the ATNR resulting in voluntary control of arm movements and the child's ability to bring objects to the midline for visual and motor exploration. At the same time, repetition of voluntary segmental rolling contributes to the inhibition of the ATNR. Segmental rolling from the supine position is initiated by the infant

98

bringing the arm opposite to the direction of rolling toward the midline while at the same time using the leg on the opposite side at first to shove off and then bring to midline in the direction of the roll. However, if the primitive reflex patterns remain dominant the sequence can be disturbed with voluntary rolling and body midline behavior failing to develop as expected. As has been noted, one indicator of bilateral integration is manual midline behavior which is simply hand movements that cross the body midline. After an infant has learned to sit, if an object is within easy reach it may be possible for the infant to cross the midline without rotation of the trunk around the body axis or turning the head. However, if an object is placed to the side and/or beyond arm's length, head turning, trunk rotation and other gross postural adjustments would be required to obtain the object. In such situations a lack of flexibility in trunk rotation, inadequate inhibition of the ATNR, or gross postural adjustments to avoid midline crossing, would result in impaired visual motor coordination and limited exploration.

Although clinical observation indicates that learning disabled children frequently demonstrate poorly integrated postural adjustments and avoidance of midline crossing, there is a need for research support for these observations. In a study using 23 developmentally normal children and an equal number of LD children, Stilwell (1981) found that the learning disabled sample demonstrated lower SVCU performance as well as less integration of postural adjustments than did the controls. Body righting reactions evaluated were rolling from supine to prone, transition from supine to standing, and equilibrium reactions. From the procedure description two examiners were used to score the postural adjustment evaluation and one of these "was generally unaware of the subject's group placement." Computation of inter-rater reliability resulted in $r = .87$. The LD children scored in the more pathological direction on each of the three postural adjustment measures as well as the SVCU. There was no significant correlation between the total postural adjustment score and the SVCU for either group. Two limitations of the study relate to the sample. A significant number of the children were six years old and this raises the question of the operational definition of learning disability. Three different measures were used to evaluate the sample's academic level and there is no report of actual scores. Both these limitations probably result in a heterogeneous sample of LD children and this has implications for replication.

Conclusion

Sensory and perceptual data has to be organized into information that contributes to cognitive organization. This review of the evaluations of bilateral integration and ocular-motor responses in LD children clearly suggests that these children have dysfunctions in sensation and perception. There is an association between postural adjustments, bilateral integration and learning disabilities. There is a possibility of such associations between signs of NBD, such as hyponystagmus, other ocular-motor responses, such as visual tracking, and problems in reading. An association is suggestive but it is not as convincing as a functional relationship.

The attempt to demonstrate a relationship between postural adjustment and manual midline behavior highlights some of the methodological issues in this area of research (Stilwell, 1981). The measurement of behavior has typically been one commonly used in clinical practice. This may be appropriate for the clinical purpose of demonstrating that the child is or is not deviant to some degree in this behavior. This is true of research using the SCSIT or the PRPA. Although the measure of behavior is sensitive enough to demonstrate the existence of deviancy, it may not be sensitive enough to establish an association or functional relationship between one type of deviant behavior, such as midline behavior, and another deviant behavior, such as postural adjustments. To demonstrate either an association or functional relationship may require more sensitive measures of behavior and more systematic manipulation of one behavior to observe the possible effect on the other behavior. In this approach one behavior becomes an independent variable while another behavior is the dependent variable. For example, laboratory research clearly indicates that there is a relationship between body stress and reflex inhibition and elicitation (Easton, 1972) and clinical evaluations also suggest such a relationship (Pothier et al., 1983; Sieg & Shuster, 1979). The typical clinical evaluation simply demonstrates the existence of the effect of stress but more systematic manipulation of stress may be needed. This may be the issue in demonstrating a relationship between postural adjustments and bilateral behavior. The SVCU does not require body rotation, and it is possible that the most effective method for demonstrating a relationship between postural adjustments and bilateral behavior in LD children is to systematically vary the requirement for body rotation while holding opportunity for contralateral use constant.

Similar methodological issues are relevant to the study of vestibular integrity and ocular-motor functions, such as visual tracking and pursuit. Although previous attempts to establish a relationship between optokinetic nystagmus and the blurring speed test in LD children (Frank & Levinson, 1976) suffer from methodological problems, the basic procedures are sound enough to allow for systematic study. For example, groups of LD children with and without hyponystagmus could be systematically studied in terms of their responses to this procedure. Considering the close association between the vestibular system and motion, a more productive area of research may be the investigation of the vestibular-ocular nystagmus in LD children. Again, hyponystagmus could be used as an indicator of vestibular integrity, and the child's performance on various perceptual tasks requiring ocular-motor responses could be the dependent variable. Another variable to be entered in such a design would be different kinds and amounts of motion experienced by the child while performing the perceptual task. The list of variables to be studied could go on, but certainly the possible effects of age would have to be investigated.

This brings up the final point in this discussion of studies to investigate the relationship between behaviors in LD children with neurobehavioral and perceptual dysfunctions. A number of previous studies have used children in the LD sample who were five to seven years old. It is highly probable that these children have been identified in kindergarten, or earlier, as performing in a school setting below the learning level of their peers. This is a failure in learning acquisition but not yet a learning disability (Lindsay & Wedell, 1982). Moreover, these children may have multiple behavior problems, as well as unique, and possibly major, sensory and perceptual dysfunctions, that differentiate them from the older sample. To establish that these younger children do not differ from the rest of the sample on variables that might influence the outcome of the study requires that age itself be treated as a variable and that multiple measures of behavior be used with the total sample. The homogeneity of children after the first grade in terms of degree of learning disability can be controlled somewhat by a variety of procedures, such as a stated discrepancy between intelligence and achievement. However, operational definitions of learning disability such as this are less applicable with the younger child. One solution to this problem is to measure the behaviors that might influence performance in school, both socially and behaviorally, to provide some control for homgeneity across age

101

level. In the investigation of the relationship between signs of NBD, control for the possible effect of age is essential. For a variety of reasons, younger children may be significantly different from older children in terms of the occurrence of particular signs, relationships between signs, and severity of signs.

Chapter 9

Neuropsychological Evaluation
of the LD Child

Introduction

Although the largest proportion of this book has been given to the evaluation of signs of NBD in LD children, this does not reflect an assumption that the occurrence of these signs in children is enough to establish their membership in the population of LD children. The focus on the evaluation procedures used to establish NBD in this text results in part from their generally being ignored or dismissed in much of the previous and current literature on learning disability. Another interrelated reason for stressing these dysfunctions is that they appear in children who also demonstrate significant dysfunctions in perception. Signs of NBD indicate a failure in sensory integration which interacts with these perceptual processing dysfunctions to contribute to the development of learning disabilities. These perceptual dysfunctions are known to have functional relationships with the acquisition of cognitive skills such as reading during the first years of the child's academic career (Satz & Friel, 1974; Silver & Hagin, 1981); the evidence for this comes from research with evaluation techniques commonly found in neuropsychological assessments (Hynd & Obrzut, 1981). Consequently, the advantages, limitations, and contributions from this area of research will be examined. Although the results of neuropsychological evaluations have consistently been interpreted as being a function of specific neuropathology, particularly the lack of integration between the hemispheres of the brain, evidence will be presented indicating that the research support for this interpretation is inadequate and that interrelated factors not related to hemispheric specialization such as attention, perceptual processing skills, and memory may also explain the failure of a child to read as expected. Finally, a direct connection will be made between NBD and these information processing functions. The clinical and research significance of this connection is fourfold: (1) Signs of NBD are part of a general systems dysfunction in sensation and perception; (2) signs of NBD and dysfunctions in sensation may be only associated with learning disability, whereas the indicators of perceptual dysfunction, because of their closer relationship to information processing and learning acquisition, have a functional relationship with cognitive skills such as reading; (3) the relationships between sensation, perception and learning acquisition can be used as reliable and meaningful criteria for forming a homogeneous subsample of LD children that (4) can be found most frequently between the ages of five and approximately nine years when learning acquisition is greatly dependent on perceptual processes.

Neuropsychological Assessment

It is instructive to note that the clinical utility of the evaluation of signs of NBD as indicators of sensory and perceptual integration (Ayres, 1969) and the neuropsychological evaluation of LD children (Doehring, 1968) both developed simultaneously and relatively recently. Both evaluation procedures are relatively new and in need of more research to support their clinical utility. It is also instructive to note that both approaches have been greatly influenced by data obtained from patients with known histories of cerebral insult or disease. Clinicians who worked directly with adult patients with known neuropathology have used signs of NBD diagnostically and as indicators for certain types of treatment (Semans, 1967). The work of these individuals had a great deal of influence on the development of evaluation procedures and the therapeutic techniques used with LD children. Their experience with neuropathology also influenced the theoretical orientation used to explain the etiology of learning disabilities (Ayres, 1972a; deQuiros & Schrager, 1979). In a very similar way, the neuropsychological evaluation of LD children grew directly from evaluation technqiues developed from clinical practice and research with adults with known neuropathology (Golden & Anderson, 1979; Selz & Reitan, 1979). The influence on neuropsychological assessments is significant in terms of the interpretation of data obtained from these procedures. Although a failure to progress academically may be the basis of the referral, a learning disability is not being evaluated but rather brain-behavior relationships. The strengths and weaknesses of this orientation to data interpretation are considerable

104

and may be understood to a degree by a discussion of the modifications and development of a battery originally developed for adults as it was revised for children.

Luria-Nebraska: Children's Revision

This battery, like the adult version, is based on the theoretical work of the neuropsychologist A.R. Luria (1973) and some knowledge of this theory is useful in an understanding of the construction of the battery and interpretation of results. All areas of the brain are characterized by their pluripotential functions. The role that a given area plays in a variety of behaviors is consistent but any given area is involved in multiple behaviors. No one given area of the brain is fully responsible for any higher cognitive skill. Higher cognitive functions such as reading are the outcome of functional systems working in concert as multiple brain units. Although brain-behavior relationships can be understood in terms of functional systems, the same overt behavior could be mediated in a number of different ways. This becomes important in interpreting test results. No particular task measures a unitary skill related to a particular brain area, but the pattern of task success and failure suggests the localization of dysfunction. In children, as development progresses and skills become more autonomous, there are systematic alterations in cortical areas used to process information and complete higher cortical functions. When the system is stable, not all areas of the brain contribute equally to all behaviors but a limited number are involved in a specific and predictable manner. If a child cannot read because of neuropathology, the functional system for reading may be impaired in one area or impaired in a number of related areas that form the functional system for reading.

The battery is composed of one hundred and forty-nine items divided into eleven behavioral scales. The Pathognomic Scale is composed of items that best discriminate normal from brain damaged children. The pattern of performance on items and scales, both qualitatively and quantitatively is used to understand the cortical integrity and localized functions (Golden & Anderson, 1979). This is similar to the procedure used to interpret the SCSIT (Ayres, 1980) and demands a great deal of clinical training, experience and competence on the part of the examiner. The validation studies for the Luria-Nebraska have followed the contrasting group design of selecting children of known CNS pathology and comparing their performance on the Battery with groups such as normals and emotionally disturbed. In general, the battery consistently discriminates between children with known CNS pathology and other groups that do not have such pathology. This is similar to the procedure used to establish the clinical utility of neuropsychological batteries with adults (Reitan & Davison, 1974). There are eleven subtests that are made up of items measuring motor skills, rhythm, tactile functions, visual skills, receptive language, expressive language, writing, reading, arithmetic, memory, and intelligence.

Brain Damage and the Developmental Sequence

Neuropsychological assessment of children evolved directly from the practice of evaluating adults. In adult neuropsychology the assumption is made by the examiner, unless there is contrary evidence, that the brain areas had been functioning adequately prior to the onset of the pathological behavior and that there is a causal link between this behavior and some dysfunctional areas of the brain. The observed behavior pathology established during the evaluation, such as impairment in short term auditory memory, is indicative of a dysfunctional area or areas of the brain. This is similar to the evaluation of signs of NBD, such as the lack of inhibition of the ATNR in adult patients who have suffered a stroke (Semans, 1967). The assumption is made by the examiner that the ATNR had been adequately inhibited prior to the stroke, and its recurrence suggests the area of the brain lesion. Because of the history of behavior change closely associated with neuropathology, the assumption of a functional relationship is supportable. As has been noted earlier, evaluation of signs of NBD in children with no known history of neuropathology presents certain problems and this is also true of child neuropsychology. A major characteristic of children is that they are constantly changing and perceptual-cognitive skills emerge at one period and continue to be modified significantly over varying periods of time. Children also develop at different rates and frequently there is not enough data from research in developmental psychology to establish what is normal variation and what is significant deviation. A major problem in the evaluation of children is knowing what perceptual or cognitive skill should exist, the level of functioning of that particular skill at any particular age range, and the relationship of that skill to other developing skills. Finally, certain assumptions have to be made regarding the environment, the major one being that there has been adequate environmental stimulation available in the child's history to adequately nurture the skills being evaluated. In the context of no documentation of insult or disease, the dysfunction in behavior observed may directly reflect a brain-behavior pathology, but it could also be an evaluation of the relationship between the child's environmental history and lack of opportunity to acquire perceptual-cognitive skills. These issues can be dealt with to a degree by establishing age related norms for samples representing a range of social class and race for the various skills being assessed by the battery. The issues here, again, are similar to those for establishing such norms for signs of NBD.

The initial normative population for the Luria-Nebraska Children's Battery (LNCB) was composed of one hundred and twenty-five children between the ages of 8 and 12 years, 12 months of age. The development of the LNCB was also guided by a theory of development and this theory can serve as a guideline for interpretation of the data obtained in an evaluation (Golden, 1981). There are four major stages in neurological organization and function between ages 8-12 that are marked by qualitative rather than quanitative changes in skills. The most basic is Stage 1, characterized by problems in atten-tion and concentration related to the function of the reticular activating system. Problems here are frequently manifested in infancy. Stage 2 is characterized by the development of the primary motor and sensory areas. These areas of the cortex contribute to such basic functions as crying, grasping, depth discrimination and reactions to auditory cues. As the CNS matures, attention and concentration stabilize, and the primary areas for motor and sensory function become more integrated, the child begins to demonstrate the behavior characteristics of Stage 3. More complex perceptions occur at this stage such as discrimination of strangers, eye-hand coordinations, and walking. Hemispheric dominance begins to develop during this stage and the most important learning occurring is within a single sensory modality. Cross-modality performance during this stage is not truly integrative but rather based on rote learning and performance. For example, learning to read is a function of word-sound association rather than comprehension. Brain injuries to particular areas experienced during this time after the child has developed consistent verbal skills, suggesting more lateralization, resemble those experienced by adults. This is not true if the injury is diffuse. In stage 4, the child is capable of integrative cross-modality learning that is a function of the parietal lobe. This stage occurs roughly between ages 5-8 and injuries in this area can have serious effects on learning acquisition and perform-ance. Depending on the degree of damage, these impairments range from mental retardation to specific learning disabilities.

The Halsted-Reitan test for children has also been developed as a modification of the adult battery. Items have been added that appear to be more appropriate for children but no underlying developmental theory has been used as a basis for item selection (Selz & Reitan, 1979). No normative studies have been published and support for the use of the Halstead-Reitan is based mostly on the contrast group des-ign. The contribution of the Halstead-Reitan or the Luria-Nebraska as a diagnostic procedure for the evaluation of children who either have documented history and medical evidence for brain injury, or who have had documented experiences and corresponding behavior changes that suggest brain injury, does not appear to be an issue. There are some research problems in this area which will be dis-cussed later, but the logic behind the use of the batteries in such cases seems clear. The issues in using these batteries with children as a means of establishing a learning disability related to brain dysfunc-tion are much more complex.

Neuropsychology and Learning Disabilities in Childhood

Children with documented neuropathology frequently demonstrate behavior problems, hyperactivity, distractibility and failure to per-form academically at a level demonstrated prior to the onset of neu-ropathology. These same behaviors are frequently found in LD chil-dren with the exception that the LD child most frequently has never had a history of expected academic success. Since LD children dem-onstrate similar behavior as those found in brain damaged children, observers have reasoned that the former group must have some degree of brain dysfunction. It is important to note that the reasoning being used is by analogy; the inference being that the observed simi-larities are sufficient to support the existence of other similarities not directly observed. An impetus for neuropsychological research with LD children came from a study of reading disabled children who were evaluated by a battery of tests measuring a range of sensory-per-ceptual functions. The results demonstrated that these LD children performed below expected levels on many of the tests that were known to be particularly sensitive to brain dysfunction (Doehring, 1968). This study was followed by a number of studies demonstrating that LD children performed below the level of those children of average academic achievement on a significant number of neuropsychological measures (Rourke & Gates, 1981). In keeping with a great deal of evaluation research with the LD population, these studies again demonstrate that LD children differ in a number of ways from developmentally normal children. In an attempt to differentiate homogeneous subgroups from the heterogeneous LD population, researchers have used neuropsychological tests to establish subgroups of children who share common problems in their mode of inference. For example, a subgroup of retarded spellers who made phonetically inaccurate spelling errors were compared to a contrast group of phonetically accurate retarded spellers on their performance on a neuropsychological battery. The rationale for this comparison is the evidence that phonetically inaccurate misspelling is characteristic of brain damaged aphasic adults. Support for the possibility that a similar brain dysfunction may be operating in this LD sample comes from the fact that children who made phonetically inaccurate spelling errors also demonstrated significantly poorer performance on tests of psycholinguistic skills than did the contrast group (Sweeney & Rourke, 1978).

Stimulated by the research with adults by Speery (1964), indicating the specialized functions of the different hemispheres of the brain, efforts have been made to establish a relationship between patterns of learning failure and particular areas of brain dysfunction. Performance on the WRAT subtests of spelling, reading decoding and arithmetic was used to form three groups: Group 1, who scored low on all three of the subtests; Group 2, who scored low on reading and spelling but scored higher on arithmetic than did the first group, although the score was still below average; and Group 3, who scored average or better on spelling and reading but scored at the same level as the children in Group 2 in arithmetic. On measures of linguistic skills the children in the first two groups performed at a significantly inferior level than was true of the third group, while this group performed at a significantly inferior level on visual-spatial tasks when compared to the other two groups. The pattern of scores was interpreted as supporting the view that the pattern of abilities and deficits found in the second group indicated a relative dysfunction of the left hemisphere but relatively adequate function of the right hemisphere. At the same time the children in the third group appeared to have a dysfunction in the right hemisphere resulting in inferior visual-spatial skills. Although children in groups 2 and 3 were equated on level of arithmetic performance, their patterns of performance on the neuropsychological batteries in both linguistic and visual-spatial skills were dissimilar (Rourke & Finlayson, 1978). Neuropsychological evaluation of LD children has moved from the demonstration of differences in the level of performance between these children and children performing as expected academically to the establishment of discriminant subgroups within the LD population itself. Batteries have also been developed that can be used to identify children at-risk for learning disabilities and neuropsychological batteries have contributed to longitudinal studies that have added to our knowledge of how learning disabilities change over time (Rourke & Orr, 1977; Satz, Friel & Goebel, 1975).

Critique of Neuropsychological Evaluation of Children

It is interesting that a number of subtests of perceptual functions found in the typical neuropsychological batteries are also found in the SCSIT (Ayres, 1980). For example, the SCSIT has subtests to measure visual-motor coordination, manual form perception, and figure ground perception, functions that are evaluated on the Halstead-Reitan batteries for children (Reitan & Davison, 1974) and the Luria-Nebraska (Golden, 1982). The SCSIT has also been used in factor analytic studies to establish subgroups within the LD population (Ayres, 1980, p. 6-15). Like the authors and developers of the neuropsychological batteries, Ayres states that brain pathology is being measured. However, research with the SCSIT is never adequately discussed in current literature reviewing advances in the this field (Hynd & Obrzut, 1981; Rutter, 1984). There are probably a variety of reasons for this but perhaps the simplest one is that the SCSIT was developed by an occupational therapist and is probably mostly used by individuals in that profession, while the neuropsychological tests have been developed primarily by behavioral scientists and used by either clinical psychologists or school psychologists. The criticisms that have been made of the use of neuropsychological tests can also be made of the SCSIT, although the latter test claims to be evaluating the sensory integration of the child rather than the child's neuropsychology.

The issues of brain behavior relationships and hypothetical constructs have already been discussed. It should be noted that neuropsychologists claim to be measuring such a relationship although it

110

is obvious that what they are measuring is behavior. The behavior observed can be a function of other variables than the brain, such as behavior problems, anxiety or depression, or the interaction of multiple environmental-biological factors (Parson & Prigatano, 1978). The psychometric qualities of the tests themselves have received considerable criticism (Reynold, 1983). For example, the Boder Test of Reading-Spelling Patterns (BTRSP) is available commercially and advertized as a test for specific learning disabilties (Boder & Jarrico, 1982). The BTRSP is designed as an assessment battery of reading and spelling skills that allows specific diagnosis of the source and typology of reading problems. The procedure can differentiate non-reading impaired from reading impaired students, and also claims to sort out dyslexic from nondyslexic reading disorders and can further discriminate within the dyslexic group itself. Two primary factors in the reading process, visual gestalt and auditory analytic functions, are evaluated and a child's performance will place him or her into one of four groups of children with (1) adequate visual gestalt reading functions and weak phonic analysis, (2) adequate phonic analysis and weak visual gestalt functions, (3) inadequacies in both phonic and visual gestalt functions, and (4) nonspecific reading disability. Although a test that can discriminate among the reading disabled population and also be used for remedial work would have a distinct advantage, an examination of the psychometric characteristics of the BTRSP suggests that the test has definite limitations (Reynolds, 1983).

Reading items for the battery were chosen from standard lists of word frequency that are quite old and probably not an adequate contemporary sample of a child's reading vocabulary. To this problem is added the fact that no normative data was actually obtained on the reading items. This means that the items may not reflect current grade level achievement and because there are no age norms, the reading items may not be ordered in terms of level of difficulty. The data obtained must also be interpreted without knowledge of the possible effects of SES and race on the child's performance. It is not possible to derive standard scores from the evaluation and a grade equivalent procedure is used as a criterion for reading problems. This procedure has been criticized as a discrepancy analysis of an individual's performance on any academic measure. In terms of the BTRSP, the procedure is insensitive to the degree of difficulty a child in the third grade has who is two years behind academically, compared to the child with the same discrepancy who is in the ninth grade. Finally, a related psychometric limitation is the scoring procedure used for obtaining a reading quotient. The reading quotient is derived as a ratio between the reading achievement score and expected grade level performance. The reading quotient has many of the same limitations as the intellectual quotient and is only used when a standard score is unattainable.

Economic Status, Race and Sensory-Perceptual Processes

The issues concerning the measurement of behavior are not unique to the BTRSP, the SCSIT, or to neuropsychological test batteries in general. There is no purpose in discussing these general issues here. However, two particular variables that may affect a child's performance on neuropsychological measures have not received enough attention. Considerable efforts have been made over the last ten years to include race and social economic status (SES) as factors in normative procedures for both the revision of intelligence tests (Wechsler, 1974) and the development of new intelligence measures (Kaufman & Kaufman, 1983). This has been done because of the evidence that these are major factors in both the development of intelligence and performance on intelligence tests (Deutsch, Katz & Jensen, 1968). However, the development of neuropsychological tests has proceeded as if the measure of brain functions are independent of the child's race or the SES of the parents. This is most obvious in both the SCSIT and BTRSP where the influence of SES and race on performance are simply not known.

There is considerable evidence that these two factors have a significant influence on sensory and perceptual functions (Amante et al., 1977; Parson & Prigatano, 1978). Acceptable normative data requires systematic sampling of an adequate number of the population of interest to produce a reliable standard to judge an individual's performance. The ratio and discrepancy number is less valuable for the clinician to use to evaluate an individual child's performance than is the standard deviation which can only be derived from normative procedures. To the degree that the norms for all children are the same, the standard score for an individual child has meaning; to the degree the norms differ for children as a function of SES and race, the standard score loses its usefulness. Performance on visual-motor tasks as an indicator of neurological pathology has a history dating back to the early use of the Bender-Gestalt (Bender, 1938). Recent research has indicated that performance on perceptual tasks requiring visual-motor coordination is a function of both race and SES. Children attending the third grade in public and parochial schools who were negative for evidence of learning disabilities were evaluated on a variety of intellectual and perceptual measures. Data was also collected on the family's SES (Amante et al., 1977) Comparing white children from lower SES groups, representing parents in the manual labor occupations, with children from upper SES groups, representing parents in professions and upper management, demonstrated that the child's performance on tests of auditory discrimination and visual perception was related to parents' SES. Children in the lower SES performed less well on these tests than did the upper SES children. The performance of black children from the lower SES was compared to white children of the same status on these same measures and the results demonstrated lower level performance by these minority children. The results suggest that level of perceptual function varies along a socioeconomic dimension. This is a complex dimension that includes a number of environmental variables as well as more biological variables, including nutrition, obstetrical and pediatric care, that may contribute to dysfunctions in the sensory and perceptual processes. These results have some bearing on the previous research on the evaluation of signs of NBD since race and SES have never been adequately measured or reported in most of these studies.

Sensory, Perceptual Dysfunction and Reading Retardation

As has been mentioned before, neuropsychological test data is interpreted as an evaluation of the functions of areas of the brain that are directly related to academic performance. This is seen when the child who is failing to read and significantly below grade level is referred for evaluation. If data from the testing shows a pattern of poor performance on tasks thought to be a function of the left hemisphere, the conclusion is made that a dysfunction in the hemisphere, or an asymmetry in the integrated functions of the hemisphere, is a causal factor in the failure to read (Gaddes, 1980). This link between areas of the brain and reading has a long history that has been stimulated in part by Orton's postulate that dyslexia was a specific disorder due to a physiological defect that prevented the normal development of unilateral cerebral dominance (Orton, 1937). The assumption of the relationship between language processing skills and the left hemisphere has been used by clinicians as a guideline in their interpretation of test results and by researchers using neuropsychological batteries to localize more specific areas of the left hemisphere that may be involved in reading skills. This assumption has also stimulated considerable research on hemispheric specialization with reading retarded children. The results of these studies do not provide consistent support for reading retardation as a function of left hemisphere pathology. In the typical design of this research, procedures are used that control for the visual or auditory input to the hemispheres. One of the major problems in this area of research is the failure of replication. For example, a number of studies using visual half field procedures have produced data indicating that reading retarded children demonstrate lower level performance on these tasks and less asymmetry than do children reading at grade level (Marcel & Rajan, 1975). However, other studies using similar procedures find that reading retarded children do not differ from controls in level of performance or evidence of asymmetry (McKeever & Van Deventer, 1975) or find that they do differ in level of performance but not in asymmetry (Bouma & Legein, 1977). Similar inconsistent results have been obtained in studies of auditory performance (Naylor, 1980). Lateralized auditory studies have used the dichotic listening technique that allows selective auditory input into one ear and one side of brain. Some studies using this procedure with reading retarded children and appropriate control children have demonstrated lowered performance and less asymmetry in the retarded sample. Other investigations have failed to find difference in asymmetry but have found lower accuracy in the retarded vs. control comparison, or have produced data indicating that retarded samples demonstrated typical ear asymmetry.

A review of laterality studies suggests that a number of methodological procedures have contributed to these inconsistent results (Naylor, 1980). Failure to adequately match reading retarded samples with contrast groups for age, level of intelligence, and within task parameters such as exposure time, makes it difficult to rule out the possible effect of these variables on performance. The visual half field studies have consistently used word recognition as the dependent variable. This procedure automatically places reading retarded children at a disadvantage since recognition of words is a function of experience as well as of reading skill. Retarded readers would generally have less exposure to printed words. Studies of auditory asymmetry using dichotically presented digits have used designs producing results that may be a function of asymmetry but could also be a function of attention, set, individual differences in strategy, and short-term memory. A consistent result of these studies is that reading retarded children are less able to remember sequences of numbers than are non-retarded readers. Based on the data generated from these experimental studies of laterally and reading retardation, it seems unwarranted to conclude that lack of hemispheric asymmetry is an adequate explanation of the failure to acquire reading competence. This lack of consistent research support also suggests that the results of neuropsychological evaluations need to be accepted with a certain level of caution. This is true of interpretations based on assumed relationships between lateralization and performance as well as specific areas of the brain and academic performance (Ross, 1973).

Information Processing and Learning Disabilities

In the analysis of learning performance, explanations in terms of brain-behavior relationship have concentrated on hemispheric specialization with language processing skills being linked to left hemisphere integrity and visuo-spatial skills being linked to the right hemisphere. An alternative analysis of learning performance is to focus on perceptual and cognitive variables that are not necessarily linked to hemispheric specialization (Naylor, 1980). An analysis of the important information processing variables in learning suggests that LD children have consistently been shown to have problems in short term memory (Rudel & Denckla, 1974). This cognitive capacity is closely related to perceptual processes such as attention, automatized visual-auditory sequencing, and visual-motor integration that are also known to be deficient in this population. Dysfunctions in these perceptual processing skills are frequently associated with signs of NBD.

Deficits in attention have been consistently demonstrated in LD populations (Tarver & Hallahan, 1974). Attentive behavior itself is a complex process that can be divided into different components for analysis. The most obvious division is between sensory modalities such as visual and auditory. In a study controlling for the effects of the simultaneous presentation through auditory and visual modalities, Senf and Freundl (1971) found that LD children could recall items in their original order as well as normal controls when a single modality was used but were deficient in recalling items in an auditory-visual combination. The results of the study suggested that a number of factors besides attention could have affected recall such as auditory distraction, auditory dominance, and deficient visual-information processing. Another approach in research on attention in LD children is to analyze the child's capacity to focus on relevant information and exclude irrelevant information. Studies with developmentally normal children indicate that selective attention increases with age, while research with LD samples indicates that the capacity to discriminate between relevant and irrelevant cues is deficient (Denny, 1974). In a study comparing reading retarded and normal controls at three different grade levels, retarded readers consistently demonstrated lower level performance on a short term memory task with higher level recall of incidental information. The data indicated that the development of selective attention on the tasks used in this study was delayed from 2 to 4 years in the retarded readers (Pelham & Ross, 1977).

These studies indicate that LD children have problems in attention and also suggest that attention itself is a complex process which needs to be understood more precisely by clinicians and researchers. Certainly studies on brain-behavior relationships must adequately control for attentional variables. Neuropsychological testing should also include an independent evaluation of attention as a control for the possible influence of this factor on the results of the evaluation. Performance on measures of auditory laterality, such as the dichotic listening task, is probably sensitive to the child's capacity to come to attention, maintain attention, and make decisions (Keogh & Margolis, 1976). None of these functions are necessarily related to hemispheric specialization.

Once a child has developed sustained attention that can be brought to bear on learning, the next major development is automatization of the perceptual processes basic to learning. In the beginning stage of reading, much of the child's conscious effort and attention is given to learning how to follow a line of words from left to right, decode each word and eventually construct meaning from the words. Automatized behaviors are ones that are so highly practiced as to require a minimum of conscious attention for their efficient execution (Boverman, 1964). Balance, walking, maintaining perceptual constancy, writing, and reading are examples of such behaviors. In previous discussions it has been pointed out that LD children who have signs of NBD frequently fail to develop adequate automatic functions, such as equilibrium reactions and compensatory nystagmus. The performance of an

116

adequate reader is characterized by a lack of attention on the reader's part of the actual process of reading. These processes have become automatized so that attention can be directed at comprehension of the content being read. This is similar to children who have automatized equilibrium reactions and can develop their motor skills for complex processes involving equilibrium such as gymnastics. The child who is a retarded reader appears to devote a great deal of attention to the process aspects of reading. The child will misread long difficult words, but also short easy ones, for even these words have failed to become reliable automatized habits. There is evidence that retarded readers demonstrate poor automatic processing skills. The tests used to measure these processes are commonly used in neuro-psychological assessments.

A frequently employed method for evaluating automatized perceptual processes is the sequential presentation of common objects or colors to a child and recording the time required for the child to name them. Reading retarded children do less well on these rapid automatized naming tests (RAN) when compared to readers, yet perform as well, and in some cases better, than readers on tasks such as block designs and mazes (Eakin & Douglas, 1971). In a comparison of a sample of LD children who had been divided in to one group of retarded readers and another group who were reading at grade level, retarded readers consistently took more time on tasks requiring the rapid automatized naming of pictured objects, colors, letters, and numbers (Denckla & Rudel, 1976). Another method for evaluating automatized perceptual processes is to present a stimulus to be discriminated among a number of similar stimuli. In this procedure the visual stimulus becomes more verbal and complex with each succeeding test and the child does not name the stimulus but indicates the discrimination by underlining the target stimulus. Again, the test requires the capacity for sequencing as well as automatized perceptual functions (Doehring, 1968). This test has been used as part of a screening battery to identify males at grade 1 and 2 who were demonstrating problems in the acquisition of reading. These children were followed for four years and performance on the underlining test predicted reading achievement (Rourke & Orr, 1977). Tests that contributed most significantly to the prediction of reading problems required that the child underline either one geometric design among a series of geometric designs or discriminate a particular sequence of four geometric designs among the same designs presented in a random order.

Automatized functions appear to differ in LD children when compared to developmentally normal children and in reading retarded children when compared to either LD children who are not retarded for reading or developmentally normal children. The failure to develop automatized functions may be related to a number of factors. The fact that failure to discriminate among a series of geometric forms predicts reading failure suggests that deficient sequencing skills as well as problems in visual-perception may be contributing factors. Proficiency at rapid automatized naming, basic to reading aloud or reading silently, requires that the child scan the presented material in sequence from left to right, make the necessary visual discriminations, decode the stimulus and name it. Before the perceptual information is modified cognitively, basic dysfunctions in compensatory nystagmus, or ocular-motor control, may contribute to lower level performance. The dysfunction may operate at this level. However, visual discrimination itself is a complex process and the failure to discriminate among a series of geometric forms, one geometric figure among others, or a particular series of geometric figures in a random series, suggests that visual-spatial perception may be dysfunctional. If one has ever tested a developmentally normal child of five, six or seven years of age on a test of reading decoding, or comprehension, one sees that the letters E A T presented separately or finally in combination are really geometric forms to be discriminated in terms of spatial relationships. The same spatial factors exist when the child is required to motorically produce with a pencil these same forms. The difference in learning to print is that the visual-spatial problems to be solved are now combined with the need to develop new patterns of motor coordination. These visual spatial-motor functions are evaluated on a number of neuropsychological batteries for children.

The child's ability to perceive spatial information and then accurately reproduce it is evaluated on the Target test (Selz, 1981). Children are shown a large stimulus figure on which are printed nine dots arranged in a square. The examiner taps 20 separate patterns on this sheet and the child is to reproduce each pattern on his own sheet of paper which corresponds to the examiner's sheet. There is a 3-second interval following each presentation by the examiner. Children reproduce the sequence and pattern of the model by connecting the dots on their paper with a pencil. The Beery test of visual motor integration (VMI) (Beery, 1982) has been used in a number of batteries, most notable in the Florida longitudinal research on learning disabilities (Satz et al., 1975). The best predictors of reading competence in this study were the finger localization test, alphabet recitation, the Peabody Picture Vocabulary Test, visual form recognition, and the VMI. The VMI consists of a series of progressively more complex geometric figures that the child must reproduce by drawing. The VMI has been standardized on children from age two to thirteen.

Neuropsychological Performance and Neurobehavioral Dysfunction

The sample of LD children described earlier in Table 2, demonstrating moderate problems in sensory integration, tonic neck reflexes, poor equilibrium reactions and hyponystagmus, were evaluated on a battery of tests that included the VMI, Target Test, Underlining Test and the RAN (Carte et al., 1984, Morrison, 1985). These studies provided estimates of the stability of the neuropsychological measures over a nine-month interval producing reliablity estimates ranging from .67 to .78. The total sample demonstrated pronounced problems in visual-motor integration as evidenced in performance one standard deviation below the mean for average performance. Children between the ages of 6 to 10 scored in the pathological range on the Target test, while a small number (8) of children age 11 functioned in the normal range. Subtest 4 on the Underlining Test, requiring the discrimination of the single geomtric form among other forms, did not discriminate between the LD sample and normal controls. All of the subtests of the Underlining Test were not given, but on subtests 8, 9, 10, and 11 that were given, the LD sample consistently performed in the pathological range. A similar pattern of below average performance occurred on the RAN subtests for use, color, numbers, and letters. The data suggests that this sample of LD children had pronounced problems on tasks requiring visual-spatial as well as visual-motor skills. It was not possible to isolate the contribution of poor motor skills to this low level performance. However, the Target test, unlike the VMI, does not require proficiency in fine motor coordination for adequate performance. That the basic deficit in this sample may be visual-spatial perception is suggested by the group's difficulty on the Target test and the failure to discriminate the particular sequence of geometric forms on the Underlining 8 subtest. Automatized functions such as measured on the RAN and Underlining test may fail to develop because visual-spatial skills are inadequate. These children had adequate language skills and capacity to think abstractly, as indicated by their vocabulary and performance on the similarities sub-test of the WISC-R.

Conclusion

The persistence of signs of NBD in LD children would result in problems in gross-motor performance requiring equilibrium reactions or gross hand-eye coordination. Correlated with these problems would be low-level body-midline performance and indicators of an undifferentiated body image. Evaluations in these areas indicating deviant development may not correlate significantly, or at all, with academic performance and this seems to be the case (Learner, 1982, Chap 3). The exception to this may be those children who demonstrate hyponystagmus and inadequate ocular-motor control. Severity of dysfunctions in these areas may be correlated with various dysfunctions in visual and visual-auditory perception. The data available suggests that the relationship between NBD and dysfunction in the perceptual processes is absolute rather than correlational: children with signs of NBD will always have varying degrees and types of perceptual problems. Processes such as visual-motor integration and visual-spatial perception are basic to the early acquisition and adequate performance of cognitive skills such as writing and reading. It is during this period of acquisition of gross-motor skills, body image, perceptual integration, and academic skills that the children of interest in this discussion begin to differ significantly from their peers.

A broad range of evaluation techniques has been discussed in these last two chapters. All these techniques can be used, and have been used, diagnostically in terms of classifying a child as being in a particular subgroup. However, the results of these evaluations can also be used to understand how the sensory and perceptual information available to the NBD child is inadequate or distorted. Understanding of this process may explain the particular reactions a child has to his own body or suggest the cause of a particular pattern of reading decoding errors. This level of understanding could suggest particular methods of intervention. Procedures to assess ocular-motor control and body midline evaluate the more gross sensory-perceptual systems which contribute to the child's capacity for information processing. Intimately related to this level of assessment is the assessment of the finer systems for information processing such as the auditory and visual. Clearly, poor ocular-motor control, and other vestibular processing dysfunctions, could contribute to the distortion of information being processed through the visual-perceptual system. However, the failure to automatize is not necessarily limited to visual-perception but can also be found in the auditory-temporal functions of LD children (Tallal & Piercy, 1973). Children with NBD appear to have multiple dysfunctions in the sensory and perceptual processing systems and many of the signs of NBD suggest early occurring vestibular processing problems. The vestibular system is a synthesizer of sensory-perceptual data from a variety of sources and functions as an automatic information processing system (Kornhuber, 1974). To adequately assess a child with NBD requires that various interrelated sensory-perceptual processes be evaluated as well. This chronic condition of having either inadequate or distorted information would result in a child being at-risk for developing other problems such as deficits in attention, hyperactivity, and social withdrawal. Clinical practice, as well as research, indicates that for the total child to be assessed and treated the evaluation must include emotional and interpersonal components.

Chapter 10

The Child's Response
to the Failure to Learn

Introduction

A great deal of effort has been devoted to defining learning disabilities in children. This effort has to be made if there is to be progress in the field, but the most significant effect of the effort has been to define learning disability by what it is not (Lerner, 1981, p. 6). The major criterion has been a discrepancy between intelligence and achievement that cannot be caused by (1) visual, hearing or motor handicaps, (2) mental retardation, (3) environmental, cultural or economic disadvantage, or (4) emotional disturbance. As can be expected of any working definition in a field that lacks sufficient empirical scientific data, this definition by exclusion has received considerable criticism. The details of the criticism are not important here, except for the exclusion of social-environmental factors or emotional disturbance as possible causal factors. Children who demonstrate signs of neurobehavioral and perceptual processsing dysfunctions will frequently come from lower SES populations. In this population, inadequate obstetrics and pediatric care, poor post-natal nutrition, as well as a host of environmental variables, (Amante et al., 1977), make the developing infant and child at-risk for the acquisition of learning disabilities based on dysfunctional sensory-perceptual-motor systems. There is simply no system of assessment available that a clinician can use to exclude such factors as possible causal agents in a child's learning disabilities. A clinical practice limited to middle and upper SES families and children might find such a definition by exclusion to be of more clinical value. Finally, sorting out emotional and behavioral disturbance as a cause or an effect can occasionally be accomplished, but generally is unsolvable in clinical practice or research. A child with a physical handicap or CNS damage, such as congenital deafness, is at-risk for the development of behavioral problems whether the impairment is chronic or more recently acquired (Fraiberg, 1977; Rutter, 1977; Schlesinger & Meadow, 1972). Such children find it difficult to adapt to the demands of their environment and the parents of these children find it difficult to respond to the emotional needs of the child or to obtain consistent satisfaction from being a parent. The child with the less obvious congenital dysfunctions in sensation and perception has a similar experience and is at-risk, although probably to a lesser degree than the physically handicapped child, for the development of learning disabilities and behavior problems. The data is consistent and the conclusion is clearly supported that children with learning disabilities demonstrate a higher rate of behavior problems than children achieving as expected (Wenar, 1982, Chap. 9). Whether or not the behavior problem is a cause or an effect of the learning disability is of a somewhat academic interest to the clinician. The issue is that to adequately help the LD child and the family, appropriate evaluation and treatment of the behavior problem must be provided.

No claim is made here that the behavior problems of the NBD child are different from other behavior problems found in the LD population. This may be the case but there is no data at this point to support such an assumption. The subsample of the LD population with behavior problems that is of concern are those children who demonstrate "equivocal" signs of CNS dysfunction, and various behavior problems that contribute significantly to their poor adjustment (Silver, 1976). In what follows, various views as to the possible etiology of the behavior problems will be reviewed. Evaluation procedures based on directly observed behaviors will be presented. These objective scales hold some promise as clinical procedures and also as quantitative measures useful for research. Finally, individual clinical case studies will be presented to illustrate the advantage of evaluating the LD child for signs of sensory, perceptual dysfunction and behavior problems.

Primitive Reflexes and Adjustments to Gravity

A number of developmental theorists have stressed the gradual emergence of body image as influential in the development of both self-observation and self-evaluation (Hoffer, 1952; Spitz, 1965). The development of an integrated body image would depend in part on adequate inhibition of primitive reflexes and maturation of postural adjustments and equilibrium reactions. The initial circular reactions that serve to provide more systematic information regarding both the child's body and the environment (Piaget, 1952) cannot occur unless adequate inhibition of the ATNR also occurs. Prior to inhibition of the ATNR, the neonate is essentially unilateral in terms of visual-motor coordination (Sherick et al., 1976). At the same time, the symmetrical tonic neck reflex serves to limit the infant's regard of data appearing in the vertical plane and consequently systematic visual-motor exploration of objects above or below the infant's head is made difficult. With the inhibition of these reflexes the infant begins to be bilateral and is capable of actively gaining sensory-perceptual-motor information at body midline as well as to the left and right, above and below. The disappearance of this asymmetrical orientation to data available on both the horizontal and vertical plane is probably the first step toward a consistent information base for a stable body image. This step is important since it signals the beginning of visual-motor coordination as a major organizer of the child's learning process.

Visually guided prehension and systematic exploration with the circular reactions play major roles in the development of sensory integration, and sensorimotor intelligence, and body image. The two year old spontaneously playing with a set of Chinese puzzle boxes is entertaining his or herself but is also developing concepts of space, volume, and sequence that would not be possible without adequate inhibition of the tonic neck reflexes. The proprioceptive, tactual, kinesthetic and visual information generated by the child as the boxes are transferred from one hand to the other at midline also contributes to the evolving body image, self-confidence, and satisfaction with self. A host of these sensory-motor encounters contributes to the differentiation of self from others. In the normal developmental sequence, this process of differentiation is greatly enhanced with the manifestation of adaptive postural reflexes and equilibrium reactions which enable the child to go to objects and obtain information. Like the inhibition of the primitive reflexes, the sense of body balance obtained from this experience contributes to the child's symmetrical orientation to the world and positive evaluation of self. The failure to inhibit the primitive reflexes and develop adequate responses to gravity has been consistently associated with varying degrees of childhood behavioral disturbance.

In terms of information theory one of the first steps in learning is getting information into the CNS. At this point, the sensory-perceptual-motor systems play a key role but the second step of integrating the information requires not only adequate functioning at the entry level but the capacity of the brain itself to organize and comprehend the data provided. Finally, the ability to store and later retrieve this information over time, as memory, is the third step which culminates in the fourth step where the acquired and stored information is adequately expressed in output and adaptive communication. In specific learning disabilities particular discrepancies in this process are of concern, such as the visual-auditory integration of a reading retarded child. Those children with NBD may lack integrative capacities at this level that contribute to their behavior problems, but they also demonstrate inadequate inhibition of primitive reflexes and vestibular processing dysfunctions that additionally contribute to their negative self-image, and behavior problems. At one level, the vestibular system can be conceived of as a major automatic information processing system that either directly modulates, or transmits a modulating influence, over sensory input at the time of motor output. Information being processed through a dysfunctional vestibular system may be distorted at the entry level resulting in impairments in cognition and disorganized emotional and interpersonal responses.

A number of investigators have observed dysfunctions in the vestibular system in behaviorally disturbed children. In heterogeneous groups that included both schizophrenic and autistic children, Bender and Faretra (1972) observed a great deal of rotating and whirling play that suggested efforts by the child to establish a dependable center of gravity. These children also demonstrated fearful reaction to rapid movement or sensations arising from gravity changes in spatial or position relationships. Clinical evaluations indicated that a signficant number of schizophrenic children showed abnormalities of posture and equilibrium (Bender, 1956). Similar clinical observations have been made with samples that were homogeneous for autism (Ornitz, 1970). This population has also been the object of a number of research investigations of postrotary nystagmus using the Barnay procedure. In general, autistic children demonstrate a hyponystagmus that appears to be related to a fundamental pathological interaction between the visual and vestibular systems. There is also correlational evidence that pathological behaviors such as hand flapping and other stereotypic behavior related to vestibular self-stimulation are associated with hyponystagmus. Comparison of a heterogeneous sample of behaviorally disturbed children with children who were either developmentally normal or neurologically handicapped, demonstrated more pathological signs of NBD in the behaviorally disturbed and neurological handicapped group than in the developmentally normal group (Friedlander, Pothier, Morrison & Herman, 1982).

Sensory and Perceptual Dysfunction and Juvenile Delinquency

One of the most consistent findings in studies of children who are juvenile delinquents is a high frequency of reading retardation (Lewis, Shanok, Balla & Bard, 1980). Reading retardation occurs at a 4% level in the population in general, while one third of children with conduct disorders are found to be reading retarded. The discrepancy between expected level and actual performance varies from two to five years. Reading retardation occurs more frequently in this population and when it does occur it tends to be a rather severe problem. Comparison of a group of minority children with a history of delinquency with a non-delinquent group demonstrated that the delinquent group performed consistently below the contrast group on visual-motor coordination tasks. Sixty-six percent of the delinquent children had abnormal Bender-Gestalt drawings whereas only 15% of the contrast group had these problems (Tarnapol, 1970). Although it has not always been possible to isolate the possible effects of such variables as SES, delinquents with learning disabilities have problems in visual sequencing, visual-motor integration, auditory-language skills and demonstrate more signs of neurobehavioral dysfunctions than do developmentally normal children (Karniski et al., 1982; Tarnopol, 1970). In another study using the Halstead-Reitan battery as well as the WAIS, a sample of delinquents was compared with a sample of non-delinquents that had been matched for age, race, sex and SES. Consistent with previous research, the delinquent subjects performed at a lower level on the neuropsychological and intelligence evaluations than did the comparison subjects (Berman & Siegel, 1976).

The results of these prevalence rate studies are consistent and suggest a relationship between learning disabilities, conduct disorders and sensory-perceptual dysfunctions. However, whether or not there is an etiological relationship between these variables remains unclear.

It could be that conduct disorders develop first and reading retardation follows, or that conduct disorders develop independently of reading retardation. In a group of children who did not develop conduct disorders until after age ten, there was no greater incidence of reading retardation than in the general population. However, there was a significant correlation between conduct problems occurring before age 10 and reading problems (Rutter, Tizard & Whitmore, 1970). In a series of studies attempting to isolate the temporal relationship between learning disability and conduct disorders, it was found that among a random sample of juvenile boys, half had learning problems prior to the onset of conduct problems. However, antisocial children who had no prior history of learning problems came from upper SES families, whereas antisocial boys with prior school problems came from lower SES families experiencing a great deal of family stress (Offord, Poushinsky & Sullivan, 1978).

In terms of the relationship between perceptual-motor problems, learning disabilities and conduct disorders, no conclusive data is available. Longitudinal studies are needed and have not been done. One of the more suggestive studies indicating a possible causal association between perceptual-motor dysfunction, learning disabilities, and behavior problems identified children entering the first grade as being at-risk for learning disabilities (Arnold et al., 1977). The procedure used to identify the at-risk sample evaluated auditory, visual perception and body image (Silver & Hagin, 1981). This sample was also evaluated academically and rated by their teachers on behavior scales. Three groups were then formed, one receiving an intervention for the perceptual delays demonstrated on the screen, one receiving academic tutoring and a group of no-contact controls. The intervention and tutoring programs took place during the first grade and the three groups were evaluated at the end of first grade and again after a year in a regular classroom program at the end of second grade. At the end of second grade the children receiving the perceptual intervention were performing at a higher level academically and intellectually than the other two groups. They were rated by their teachers as having fewer behavior problems than the children in the other groups. Specifically, the intervention group improved on ratings of hyperkinetic, unsocialized and shy-inept behavior while the two control groups became significantly worse on depressed, dissocial and antisocial behavior (Arnold, Smeltzer & Barnebey, 1981). These studies suggest that perceptual-motor delays contribute significantly to the development of both learning disabilities and behavior problems.

Children who demonstrate antisocial behavior may also have other behavior problems that represent a generalized problem in adjustment. The results also suggest that children with perceptual delays may react negatively to the typical classroom instruction with the result that they become depressed and antisocial. At a more positive level, the study also suggests that early intervention for specific perceptual delays may prevent the development of both academic and behavior problems.

Behavior Problems in LD Children

Signs of NBD often found in LD children are frequently found in schizophrenic, autistic, and other emotionally disturbed children. Children with conduct disturbance also frequently have sensory-perceptual dysfunctions and reading retardation. It is probable that if these delinquent children had been evaluated for other signs of behavior disturbance, their antisocial behavior would have been one among a cluster of problem behaviors. One possible behavioral outcome in children with learning disabilities is that they develop behavior problems such as conduct disorders, attention deficits, hyperactivity, and depression, and if they are members of minority groups and/or from a lower SES, they may become juvenile delinquents. Having perceptual-motor problems and a learning disability make the child vulnerable to the development of a range of behavior problems. In addition, and if she or he are minority members and/or members of lower SES families, this background serves as a stress factor contributing to make the child even more vulnerable to behavior problems. A host of variables may contribute to the development of behavior problems in the child with NBD and learning disability. Viewing the child's development in terms of differentiation and integration may help in the understanding of the process.

During the postnatal period, the infant's response to the environment is undifferentiated and with time becomes more differentiated and at the same time integrated (Witkins et al., 1962). Specific perceptual modalities must become more differentiated from one another before they can function in an articulate, integrated response. To fully understand this, recall the behavior of the post-natal infant from birth to 3-4 months. Every turn of the body and shift in gravity elicits primitive reflexes and gross postural adjustments while any signifi-

129

cant auditory or visual stimulus change elicits gross behavior changes. With the shift in dominance in primitive reflexes, postural adjustments, and equilibrium reactions, the child gains more voluntary control of the body. Perceptual systems stabilize first within one modality and then gradually between modalities: the five-month-old looks at the source of sound and visually guided prehension occurs. This is obviously just the beginning of a process that will be instrumental to the child at age seven being able to look at a sequence of new and poorly understood symbols and articulate the arbitrary sounds that the child is told are the only ones that are to be associated with the symbols. There is a cognitive component to this decoding and comprehension process but at this point of acquisition it is a perceptual task greatly dependent on the differentiation and integration of the various perceptual modalities.

The process of differentiation and integration is dependent on adequate information being perceived at the point of entry. This is basic to the process of intersensory integration which functions to synthesize information coming from the various perceptual sources. It is also basic for coordinated motor functions, such as the circular reactions, that is the major mechanism in assimilation and accommodation (Piaget, 1954) and differentiation and integration (Witkins et al., 1962). If the data at input is inadequate because of the disruptive effect of NBD, integration may fail to reach fully adaptive levels because the process of differentiation is arrested. Behaviorally, this is seen in the failure of these children to perform as expected on tasks of visual pursuit, or visual sequencing, as well as a host of tasks requiring automatized functions (Boverman, 1964). Differentiation and integration at the level of the tonic neck reflexes and equilibrium reactions, as well as the auditory-visual level, is required before automatization can occur. The child with NBD fails to develop automatized behaviors and must make a conscious effort to modulate both incoming information and adaptive responses for the efficient execution of everyday activities.

Differentiation is observed in the child who can perceive several simultaneously-received discrete stimuli independently and combine the significant information to make an adaptive response. A disruption of differentiation is observed in uncritical overgeneralization to various aspects of the information available or an indiscriminate response to only one segment of the total information presented. The source of information may originate internally, such as a sense of the body in equilibrium with gravity, or from the environment, such as a

130

teacher presenting a printed word and making the sound of the word, or as is usually the case, the source of information is a constant flux of internal and external stimuli. All the operations of later developing intelligence require the perceptual integration of figure-group relationships, spatial orientation, sequentially presented data, and causal order. Adaptive functioning at this level is basic to short and long term memory as well as the operations of abstract thought. Lack of sensory and perceptual differentiation will disrupt this developmental sequence. The child experiences chronic and continued frustration which results in behavioral problems that may be first observed in school but have probably been developing for some time. For example, the children identified as being at-risk for learning disabilities at the beginning of first grade were already being seen by their teachers as being more hyperkinetic, and behaviorally disturbed than their peers (Arnold et al., 1977). Over the two year interval of the study, the children who did not receive a perceptually based intervention continued to be seen by their teachers as hyperkinetic and behaviorally disturbed. The intervention program used in this study establishes differentiation and automatization in auditory and visual perception before the child is trained to integrate the different modalities (Silver & Hagin, 1981). The disruption in the learning process is of a pre-academic origin but in perceptual functions that are basic to early academic learning and performance. Lack of differentiation may be directly manifest in attention deficits and hyperactivity. The chronic frustration experienced by the child is not adequately reduced by the typical behaviors parents use to encourage learning in their child such as modeling. An early cycle of mutual frustration emerges. The child may become a behavior problem, and a focus for family conflicts.

Behavioral Problems in LD Child with Neurobehavioral and Perceptual Dysfunctions

Although no claim is made that LD children with the complication of neurobehavioral and perceptual dysfunctions are uniquely vulnerable to particular patterns of behavioral problems, this could be the case. Previous research has clearly suggested that perceptual dysfunctions may contribute to the development of behavior problems but the children in these studies have not been independently evaluated for signs

131

of NBD (Arnold et al., 1977). There has been research investigating the relationship between vestibular processing dysfunction and behavioral problems in LD children, but the interpretation of the results of these studies has been limited by two interrelated issues in the research design: criterion for inclusion as learning disabled and the measurement of behavioral problems. Using what was described simply as a sample of LD children who demonstrated behavioral problems, Jung-Finacchaaro (1974) found a borderline statistical relationship (p = .10) between a factor on the Devereux Elementary School Behavior Rating Scale and degree of postural dysfunction. The behavioral scale used has respectable measurement characteristics (Spivack & Swift, 1967) but the inadequate description of the LD sample and the weak statistical relationship would make it difficult to replicate the study. In a later study, a behavioral scale with no reported reliability or validity data was used to establish that hyponystagmus was associated with socially inappropriate behaviors in a subgroup of LD boys (Ottenbacher, Watson & Short, 1979). Again, the sample was inadequately described as being composed of children who had either a medical and/or an educational diagnosis of learning disability. The use of two different evaluation procedures, that are not equivalent, could result in a heterogeneous sample. An additional problem is that the age range was from four to nine years. As has been noted previously, it is very difficult to adequately assess learning disabilities in preschoolers (Lindsay & Wedell, 1982).

There is considerable evidence that similar to the term "learning disabled" the term "behaviorally disturbed" does not describe a homogeneous subsample of the population of children. The two studies just described highlight the problems in definition and measurement that are characteristic of research with LD children and children with behavior problems. One of the major handicaps in research and communication in childhood psychopathology has been the lack of a standardized, objective, and reliable way of describing and classifying behavior disorders. The problems of the reliability and validity of psychiatric diagnosis for children such as the procedures recommended in DSM III (American Psychiatric Association, 1980), have been adequately noted (Wenar, 1982, p. 80-84). Some of these problems have been the stimulus for the development of a multivariate statistical approach in which statistical methods are used to define more objectively the degree of pathology as well as establish relatively independent categories of behavior problems. This approach has its own problems but does hold some promise of providing a measurement system that might clarify questions regarding etiology, prognosis, and appropriate treatment of childhood behavior problems.

Quantitative Measures of Behavior Problems

The Child Behavior Checklist (CBCL) has received a great deal of objective support in its development and in its application in both clinical and research studies (Edelbrock & Achenbach, 1980). The development of the CBCL illustrates the typical methods used in the development of behavior scales. As a first step, descriptions of pathological behavior were collected from various sources. The descriptions were of observable behavior that reduced the effect of observer bias, and interpretation. Examples are: child argues a lot, complains of loneliness and runs away. A variety of statistical procedures were employed to produce a checklist of 118 items that was filled out by parents of 1800 children referred for mental health services. This data was factor analyzed to produce both narrow band or specific clusters of behavior problems, and wide band or more general clusters of problem behaviors. Examples of narrow band behaviors are somatic complaints and depression, while examples of wide band behaviors are more general problems with self, or internalization, and problems and conflicts with the outside world, or externalization. Continued research with the CBCL has resulted in different norms for age intervals, as well as separate scales and norms for males and females. Empirically derived patterns of problems for males and females of particular age ranges were also established. For example, boys and girls ages 6 to 11 have distinctive patterns on the separate scales of the CBCL for somatic complaints, hyperactivity, and delinquent behavior.

For boys between the ages of six to twelve the CBCL can be used to assess the following narrow band behaviors: (1) Schizoid, (2) Depressed, (3) Uncommunicative, (4) Obsessive-Compulsive, (5) Somatic Complaints, (6) Social Withdrawal, (7) Hyperactive, (8) Aggressive, and (9) Delinquent. The parents of 37 LD boys from the sample described earlier (Carte et al., 1984) completed the CBCL and the data from these children was compared with a sample of developmentally normal boys of the same age. A series of t-tests with each of the nine scales for the two samples established a significant difference on two of the scales. The T-score for the LD boys on social withdrawal was 60.32, while the same score for the normal boys was 53.7.

The difference between the means was significant (t = 2.96, df = 72, p < .01). For the hyperactive scale, the T-score for the normal sample was 52.8 and the same score for the LD boys was 60.81. The difference between the means was significant (t = 2.96, df = 72, p < .01). The LD sample was divided by mean split on these two scales and comparisons were made between these two groups on their scores on tests of postrotary nystagmus, equilibrium reactions, and visual motor integration. The more behaviorally disturbed boys on both scales performed less well on the test of visual-motor integration but did not differ in nystagmus duration or equilibrium reactions. To further study the relationship between hyperactivity and social withdrawal, the boys scoring above or below the mean on each scale were examined in terms of their relative placement in the group. Of seventeen children, thirteen who scored below the mean on hyperactivity also scored below the mean on social withdrawal. Of twenty children, thirteen who scored above the mean on hyperactivity also scored above the mean on social withdrawal. A contingency coefficient obtained from this data was significant (C = .38, p = .01). The parents of these boys had a definite tendency to see them as both hyperactive and socially withdrawn.

Behavioral scales, such as the CBCL, that have satisfactory reliability and research indicating their validity, have significant positive features in both their clinical and research application. There are a number of behavioral scales which measure fewer dimensions of behavior than the CBCL. These scales may be more useful than a more general measure in some situations. Of particular relevance for LD children are behavioral measures of hyperactivity (Conners, 1970), attention deficit disorder (Henker & Whalen, 1985) and childhood depression (Kovacs & Beck, 1977). Although a discrete measure may be useful at times, it should be understood that it is probably rare that a child has one particular behavior problem but has a cluster of interrelated behaviors that are manifest as multiple problems. For example, LD children who are hyperactive will frequently exhibit problems in attention as well as a variety of noncompliant, asocial, poorly controlled behaviors that are irritating to peers and adults alike. Other prominent behaviors may be aggression and poor peer relationships with lowered self esteem and emotional lability. Generally, behavior scales can be filled out by individuals such as teachers and parents who are not necessarily trained as specialists in childhood psychopathology. The scales can be used in a variety of settings such as a school room or home. This is a particular advantage in that variations in the child's behavior may be significant in terms of possible causes of behavior or the generality of the disturbance. The scales are also useful in terms of measuring behavior change over time. Probably one of the major concerns in using behavior scales is that although the scales attempt to focus on observable behavior, the possibility of observer bias may still affect both the reliability, and perhaps validity of the ratings. The best examples of this can be found in studies in which discrepancies occur between a child's rating of his or her own behavior and the parents rating of that child's behavior, and the ratings of mothers and fathers of a child's behavior. In studies utilizing children's depressive symptom scales, researchers have found low correlations between parent completed and child completed scales (Kazdin, French, Unis & Esveldt-Dawson, 1983). In a recent study using the CBCL with a sample of parents whose children were not having academic or behavior problems, mothers rated sons higher on symptoms than did fathers, while these same parents did not differ in their ratings of their daughters (Jensen et al., 1983).

At the level of input, data processed by the sensory and perceptual system of the NBD child is incomplete, distorted, or not integrated. This is a chronic state existing at birth and results in a lack of differentiation in the child's response to internal states and learning opportunities. The interaction of these factors results in the child being at-risk for the development of both behavior problems and learning disabilities. Behavioral scales can be used to evaluate the behavior of the LD child. Since behavior problems frequently occur in LD children, some evaluation in this area should always be done. Behavior scales do not require special training and can be completed by any adult who has a consistent opportunity to observe the child. Although there is considerable research using groups of children that demonstrate the utility of behavioral scales, perhaps individual case examples can best illustrate their use with LD children who also have neurobehavioral and perceptual dysfunctions.

Case Illustrations: Andy and Beth

Both of these children are from middle-class families. Andy has been in the First Grade for approximately six months. His teacher has been concerned both with his academic performance and behavior problems in the classroom. She has not identified him as an LD child, partially because of his age, but was concerned that he was possibly "developmentally delayed" and at-risk for developing learning disabilities. He was referred for a thorough evaluation in order to plan a suitable educational experience for a child who appeared to be bright but immature.

The results of the evaluation are summarized in Table 4. It is noteworthy that this is an extremely bright boy who should, considering his intelligence, do well on academic tasks. His unusual level of intelligence should be kept in mind in evaluating his academic achievement. Frequently children such as this become identified as relatively learning disabled, in that they may function at grade level but this level of achievement is below the level expected for their intelligence. Based on Andy's performance on reading decoding this might be the case with him. Grade level reading on the WRAT decoding test used here is reflected in a standard score of 100 (Jastek, 1978). His score of 105 places him a little above the 60 percentile rank whereas his intelligence test score is in the upper 90th percentile rank. Given simple letters and words to identify, Andy functions at a level which would not be of concern at this point in his academic career. However, when he must read a series of words and demonstrate comprehension, his level of performance is not only relatively low considering his basic intelligence, but absolutely low. Average performance on the Gates McGinitie produces a normal curve equivalence score (NCE) of 50 with a SD = 21. Andy's NCE score of 29 places him significantly below grade level.

Based primarily on his low reading comprehension, Andy was further assessed for visual-motor integration on the Developmental Test of Visual-Motor Integration (Beery, 1982). His standard score of 10 is in the average range, an indication that his low reading comprehension is probably not related to lack of integration between visual-motor functions. Interpretation of Andy's performance on the Target Test and the Underlining Test is complicated by the fact that although these tests are considered neuropsychological measures, they have not been adequately normed and do not have standard scores for children of this age. The Target Test measures perception, transposition, and comprehension of visual-spatial relationships, while the Underlining Test assesses speed and accuracy of visual-discrimination for various kinds of verbal and nonverbal visual stimuli presented singly and in combination. The Underlining Test also assesses short term memory and sequencing ability. Comparison of Andy's performance on these tests indicates that he is consistently performing below the level of children of similar age who were not

Table 4: Case Illustrations

Andy (Ca = 85 mo.)

Intelligence	Decoding	Comprehension	PNT Total Score	Tonic Neck Reflex	Visual-Motor	Target	Underlining: 3-4-5-6	Equilibrium
138	105	29	8 sec.	3	10	6	7 6 4 6	4

CBCL	Depression	Obs.Comp.	Soma.	Socwd.	Hyper.	Aggr.	Delinq.
T-Scores:	57	56	62	57	56	42	50

Beth (CA = 108 mos.)

Intelligence	Decoding	Comprehension	PNT Total Score	Tonic Neck Reflex	Visual-Motor	Target	Underlining: 3-4-5-6	Equilibrium
105	101	21	3 sec.	1	6	19	4 5 8 11	6

CBCL	Depression	Soma.	Socwd.	Hyper.	Aggr.	Delinq.
T-Scores:	31	80	16	54		55

identified as having academic problems (Knights & Norwood, 1980; Rourke & Orr, 1977). This suggests that a basic visual-spatial dysfunction is interfering with the development of automatized visual perception and sequencing skills which may be contributing to Andy's inadequate reading comprehension.

Andy perhaps typifies those children who have perceptual dysfunctions in existence prior to school experience that contribute to their academic problems in First Grade (Arnold et al., 1977). He also demonstrates signs of NBD. Andy was evaluated on the PRPA, and at age seven a child should not demonstrate the tonic neck reflex or problems in equilibrium reactions under the conditions of minimal stress employed during the PRPA procedure. This means that Andy should have been evaluated as having zero scores for primitive reflexes and equilibrium reactions. During the postrotary nystagmus evaluation, Andy expressed reluctance to participate once he was informed that he would be rotated. He said that he did not like to "spin" and would get dizzy and sick. At the end of the procedure he said he did not enjoy it but he did not demonstrate any signs of vertigo. His total nystagmus duration score is extremely low, and considered in the context of his lack of adequate inhibition of the tonic neck reflex and inadequate equilibrium reactions, suggest major vestibular processing dysfunctions.

The analysis of the data to this point indicates that Andy is significantly delayed in development in visual perception and sensory integration. This would contribute to his being at-risk for academic problems, which seems to be the case, and for behavior problems as well. He has only been in the First Grade for approximately six months and he is already demonstrating a tendency toward behaviors that will not contribute to his future adaptation. Children demonstrating no deviant behaviors for their age receive T-scores on the CBCL of 50. This score indicates that 50% of the population are functioning at this level. Examination of the ratings of Andy by his parents suggest that he is somewhat more depressed and socially withdrawn than most children of his age. Seventy-five percent of the population is rated lower in these areas than Andy. Feeling unhappy about himself and isolated socially, this seven year old boy complains to his parents about a variety of somatic problems such as pains, headaches, and being over tired. He makes these somatic complaints more frequently th n 85% of the population of boys his age. A more thorough evaluation would be needed in order to assess how the family is interacting around these behavior problems as well as Andy's tendency to be obsessive-compulsive and hyperactive. In any case, it is clear that Andy demonstrates neurobehavioral and perceptual dysfunction and in his first year of academic learning is failing to comprehend what he reads. His behavior problems, as seen by his parents, are probably occurring at school and further contribute to his difficulties in that setting. An adequate program of intervention would include efforts directed at his educational and behavioral difficulties.

Beth is nine years old, has been identified as LD and placed in a special class. She has average intelligence, and like Andy, her decoding skills are appropriate. It is interesting that the decoding test from the WRAT has been used in a large number of research studies on reading retardation and that both Andy and Beth might not be identified as having problems in reading if they were screened on this measure alone. However, when evaluated for the more complex process of reading comprehension, Beth is found to be functioning more than one standard deviation below the expected level. Beth's ability to comprehend and reproduce, visually presented sequential spatial relationships is adequate, as evidenced by her performance on the Target Test, but her performance on the test of visual-motor integration indicates a significant dysfunction in this area. This problem could interfere with her ability to write as well as read. That this problem may be one more of visual sequencing from left to right, than of motor output, is suggested by her difficulty in visually discriminating single nonsense letters, and gestalt figures on tests 3 and 4 of the Underlining Test.

Beth's response to being evaluated for equilibrium reactions probably reflects a dimension of her coping strategies which might not be measured on a behavior scale such as the CBCL. As she took off her shoes to get on the platform, she reported that she had problems with balance in the past, but since she started dancing lessons this was no longer a problem. As she proceeded through the assessment, she talked a great deal, more to herself than the examiner, about how well she could do each task. She also talked to herself about what she should do: "Keep your arms out and look at the picture on the wall." Even as she was having difficulties at standing balance using both legs, she was saying that perhaps she could do better on one leg since that is how they practiced in dance class. Her inadequate equilibrium reactions, and extremely depressed nystagmus duration, suggest rather pronounced vestibular processing problems. Lack of adequate stress in the PRPA procedure, and perhaps maturation, may account for adequate inhibition of the tonic neck reflexes.

In terms of the parents' perception of Beth, she is seen as a child who constantly makes somatic complaints. This appears to be the only problem, as far as the CBCL measures the parent's view of Beth, but it is very significant. For example, the parents evaluate Beth as making more somatic complaints than 99% of girls her age. Since it must be difficult for the parents always to know when the complaints actually reflect physical symptoms, this behavior problem must add considerable stress to the family. There was no evidence that Beth had a physical illness. It is likely that Beth uses the denial observed during the evaluation for equilibrium reactions, as well as somatic complaints, as a way of dealing with her academic problems at school. Again, an intervention program should address both Beth's academic and behavioral problems.

Conclusion

There is evidence that some children with severe emotional problems and antisocial behaviors also have signs of neurobehavioral and perceptual dysfunction. The assumption has been made that these signs contribute in significant ways to the development of both autism and childhood schizophrenia. LD children in general demonstrate more behavioral disturbances than is commonly found in children, and often, such as in the case of Beth, these problems can be severe. The attempt to define the failure of a child to learn only as a learning disability when variables such as behavior problems and environmental stress cannot be possible causes, has limited usefulness in actual practice. The important issue is to evaluate the LD child for possible behavior problems. If behavior problems do exist, it is naive to think that simply addressing the learning disability will change the behavior problem. Both are interacting behaviors in the same child. Andy's moderate depression and tendency toward social withdrawal will interefere with his attempts to learn and his failure to learn will contribute to the behavior problems. Children with neurobehavioral and perceptual dysfunctions will frequently have difficulties learning as well as interrelated behavior problems, and these difficulties will exist prior to the child beginning school. Children who later develop learning disabilities based on a different etiology, such as a psycholinguistic deficit (Velluntino, 1977), may be more vulnerable to behavior problems once they have entered school and experienced failure. Behavioral scales offer many advantages as objective estimates of both the degree and type of behavior problem in the child as observed by either parents or teachers. At times this information can be useful in defining areas of concern and in suggesting ways for dealing with the behaviors. A sensitive teacher, trained to work with LD children can refer to a variety of behavior management techniques in helping the child learn (Lerner, 1981, Chap 12). Frequently, parents are so involved with their child that outside consultation and help is needed. In cases where the child demonstrates more severe behavior problems, such as Beth, both parent and child may need intervention focused on the behavior problems (Silver, 1976). With children such as Andy, who is clearly at-risk for developing learning disabilities and behavior problems, early clinical intervention for the child's disturbed behavior, as well as attention to his failures to learn, may function to prevent more serious problems from developing.

Chapter 11

Evaluation and Intervention

Introduction

Considerable effort has been made in the previous discussions to establish the validity of the data indicating that a significant number of LD children have a particular pattern of sensory and perceptual dysfunctions. These dysfunctions result in information being distorted at input and at the level of sensory integration. The assumption is made that the child's failure to learn is based primarily on this failure in information processing rather than more cognitive variables such as psycholinguistic impairments. Although the data supporting the existence of these particular patterns of dysfunction cannot be ignored, it is clear that conceptual problems exist. Probably the most basic problem is the lack of evidence that all children having these dysfunctions will also have learning disabilities. A variation of this is the lack of evidence that all children having signs of NBD will also have perceptual dysfunctions. One could go on with the possible combinations that would alter the credibility accorded to the existence of this pattern of dysfunction and its relationship to learning disabilities. The only answer is continued research that will add to our evaluation procedures and knowledge in this general area. Research on evaluation is valuable in itself since the data generated can add to or modify existing knowledge of the variables contributing to learning disabilities in children and possibly suggest intervention procedures.

It has been noted that LD children differ in many ways from developmentally normal children and that at any point in time one or more of these differences have been seen as contributing to the LD child's failure to learn (Kinsbourne, 1985). One conclusion from this view is that dysfunctions at the level of sensory and perceptual processes are epiphenomena having no, or limited, bearing on the actual failure to learn (Feagans, 1983). The main argument against this position is that major theories of learning all have in common the importance placed

143

on sensory and perceptual processes in learning acquisition (Bijou & Baer, 1960; Hebb, 1949; Piaget, 1952). There is a considerable amount of empirical data based on accepted research to support this theoretical view (Spears & Hohle, 1967). Probably the most persistent argument against the contribution of sensory and perceptual dysfunctions to a child's failure to learn is the inconsistent results obtained in research studies on the effects of sensory and perceptual intervention on learning disabilities.

In terms of logic it is clear that either the existence of the dysfunction, or its contribution to a learning disability, cannot be validated by the effects of sensory and/or perceptually based intervention techniques. The possible reasons that an intervention technique would not be effective may be found in research design issues, such as sample size and representation, adequate control groups, and data analysis. A number of critiques of perceptual-motor training have addressed such issues and concluded that there is no firm evidence that perceptual-motor training is a significant addition to a LD child's curriculum (Kavale & Mattson, 1983). Based on inconsistent research support, the argument has been made that time in such training is time that would better be used on academic activities directly relevant to the learning problem. For a teacher or school administrator these are very real issues since the child's education is their major responsibility. The issues related to outcome research on perceptual-motor training have been adequately reviewed elsewhere (Mann, 1970; Velluntino et al., 1977) and will not be addressed again here. There are similar issues in the research on outcome effects of perceptual-motor training and sensory integration therapy. Some of these issues will be addressed in the following review of the outcome research of sensory integration therapy.

Sensory Integration Therapy

This therapy has been applied with a variety of clinical populations with varying effects (Ottenbacher, 1982). Naturally, the population of concern here is LD children. However, like perceptual-motor training, the application of sensory integration (S.I.) therapy in general has generated considerable controversy. Although acceptance or rejection of the therapy will eventually be based on accumulated data, this process itself will be influenced by the social climate of the times. This climate will also affect the professional acceptance of the evaluation procedures, or the existence of a syndrome based on the evaluation procedures. For example, based on the clinical evaluation of cerebellar-vestibular dysfunctions, Levinson (1983) prescribes medications usually used for sea sickness for individuals with reading retardation. This practice, which is not based on sufficient research data, has generated a negative reaction to both the diagnostic and treatment procedures advanced by this clinician (Arnold, 1983). A similar reaction has occurred to both the evaluation and intervention procedures used in SI therapy. These are not simply academic issues since the actual therapeutic value has been openly questioned. If the procedure has no demonstrable positive effect, why should a child's time be spent in such activity and why should time, space and financial resources be allocated? Such arguments have been made regarding the use of SI therapy for LD children (Lere, 1981) and in a similar vein, but to a lesser degree, for children with other handicapping conditions (Jenkins & Sells, 1984). At the same time, advocates of the therapy continue their endorsement (Ottenbacher, 1982; Price, 1977), apparently based on different data. These factors related to the social climate, and probably professional training and economic loss or gain, influence research, interpretation of data, and application of results.

One of the major issues in outcome research is the operational definition of the type of intervention provided and the description and definition of the sample receiving the intervention. An example of a lack of operational definition is seen in one of the frequently referenced studies showing the positive effect of S.I. therapy with LD children having hyponystagmus. The total description of the intervention is: "It [therapy] stressed vestibular, tactile and proprioceptive stimulation and activation of mechanisms involving these systems" (Ayres, 1978). It would not be possible to replicate the intervention used in this study with this description. At its most general level, SI therapy employs procedures for sensory stimulation and adaptive responses involving total body movement. The actual techniques may vary as a function of the therapist's training, experience, and creativity, but to be considered SI therapy the techniques should include combinations of vestibular proprioceptive and tactile stimulation in a planned, controlled sequence. The basis of the sensory stimulation is an assumed developmental sequence of neurophysiological mechanisms that is positively influenced by this intervention. SI therapy works to effect progressive organization of the LD child's brain in the direction of that of a developmentally normal child (Ayres, 1972a). The goal of the therapy is to improve the way the brain processes and organizes sensation and not to teach specific perceptual-motor or academic skills. Interventions that provide perceptual-motor training should not be considered as SI therapy. The possible positive effect on perceptual-motor dysfunctions and academic failure would come about indirectly as the improved organization of the brain was manifest in inhibition of reflexes, more adequate equilibrium reactions, normalized nystagmus, and more efficient ocular-motor control. As a consequence of the progress in sensory integration, the child's perceptual-motor and academic performance would eventually improve. An outcome study therefore should include measures of sensory integration, perception, and academic achievement.

As has been noted previously, one of the signs of vestibular dysfunction is hyponystagmus, and clinical observations (Ayres, 1972a), as well as research (Morrison & Sublett, 1983), have established that LD children frequently demonstrate this sign. Since SI therapy directly treats vestibular dysfunctions, it would be logical to assume that LD children with hyponystagmus, or any deviant nystagmus, might be ideal candidates for this intervention. LD children who had been referred to a rehabilitation center by either medical or educational personnel were evaluated for nystagmus duration with the PNT (Ottenbacher, Short & Watson, 1979). The children received SI therapy of relatively shorter or longer durations. The results suggested that after therapy children with hyponystagmus tended to show increased duration scores while children with hypernystagmus, and children who obtained what was referred to as "medium" nystagmus scores, tended to demonstrate reduction in duration. These post-test changes were more apparent following relatively long therapy rather than short therapy. There are a number of issues in the design of this study, typical of other studies in this area of research, that limits the interpretation of the results. As has been noted in a number of studies previously reviewed, the description of the LD sample is inadequate for any possible efforts at replication. Another issue is that a number of children in the sample had to be less than six years-six months old. Again, as previously noted, it could be argued that these children are potentially learning disabled by presenting the data for a significant discrepancy between performance on some preacademic task and intelligence, but without some type of control along these lines, it is not possible to say what this young group was like in terms of learning problems. A major concern is that LD children who at pre-test demonstrated what was termed "medium" duration scores were scoring in the normal range (22.5 sec.) After long term therapy

146

their nystagmus duration had fallen to what is often considered hyponystagmus (10.1 sec.) and clearly below the normal reaction time. Duration scores from this group were included in the data analysis and the results were interpreted by the authors as indicating the positive effects of intervention.

The major support for the effect of SI therapy on academic performance comes from two research studies. A sample of 148 children identified as learning disabled by their placement in the public school system were divided into therapy and no therapy groups (Ayres, 1972b). Although approximately one half of these children received therapy it was decided that only 68 children, or 46%, were really appropriate candidates for therapy. This decision was based on a diagnostic system with no reported reliablity. This system was applied at the point of initial evaluation and used in a procedure in which "arbitrary regression scores were set below which a child's score had to fall to qualify him for inclusion in the statistical analyses" (Ayres, 1972b, p. 340). The procedure used for the final selection of children to be included in the data analysis is so vague that replication of the study would not be possible. The final sample included 31 children in the therapy group and 37 control children. Again, nothing is mentioned of such potential independent variables as SES, or sex distribution. In terms of pre-test academic levels and levels of sensory integration, the sample is adequately described and the therapy and no therapy groups were equated on these variables. Post-testing occurred five months after therapy was terminated and the results indicated that children having generalized sensory integration problems (N = 30) improved on the WRAT decoding test (Jastek, 1978), while those children with auditory-language disorders (N = 12) improved both on WRAT decoding and spelling as well as the Slosson Oral Reading Test. All these results are based on pre-post test gain scores compared with the no-therapy children.

The results of this study generated considerable interest in the use of SI therapy for children with academic problems. Typical of studies using a two group design, with one group being a no-contact control, the study could be criticized for not having a third group receiving an alternative intervention or social attention. A limited control for the effects of social attention alone would have been a pre-post test analysis of the data available from the scores of the sensory integration evaluation. If the children had also improved at the level of sensory integration as well, it would be less probable that increased amounts of social attention alone could explain the results. The fact that there

147

was at least a 5-month interval before post-testing occurred is a major flaw in the design. The reason for the decision is not given and no statement is made indicating that the two groups were actually equated on this variable. The statement of "at least five months" means that some post-testing occurred beyond this time and the range of this interval is unknown. Despite some of the limitations in the study, the results indicated that a non-academic activity which treated neurobehavioral and perceptual dysfunctions resulted in improved auditory-language skills and academic achievement.

In a systematic replication of this research, 46 LD children received approximately six months of SI therapy, while an equal number of control children received academic instruction only (Ayres, 1978). It is interesting that in contrast to the previous study in which children were selected by a quantified clinical evaluation as candidates for therapy (Ayres, 1972b), these children were not selected by this procedure. The two major criteria for being placed in therapy were academic achievement below intellectual capacity and inability of a child with adequate intellectual ability to profit from placement in a regular class. If the previous evaluation system was expected to gain some acceptance it should have been more clearly described and used again in this study. Post-test comparisons between the two groups revealed no effect on a variety of perceptual, language, and academic measures. However, a separate analysis of 23 children with hyponystagmus assessed at pre-test with the PNT, indicated that these children had greater gains in scores from the three subtests of the WRAT, than a comparable hyponystagmus group of control children. Change scores from the WRAT were compared with the median change score for both groups combined. Scores of 8 of the therapy group and 15 of the no therapy group fell below the group median producing a chi square signficance at greater than the .05 level.

Certainly this result is less robust than the results obtained in the previous study. A number of auditory-language tests, including the Slosson, which had been used previously, were administered to the children and entered in the pre-post test analysis of the hyponystagmus subsample. The children receiving therapy did not differ over time when compared with controls. The failure to replicate the results of the previous research is not discussed, although considerable attention is given to the possible relationship between auditory-language functions and the vestibular system. There are major problems in the design of this study. The WRAT scores are used as a dependent variable and the actual scores are not presented. It is possible that these scores were in the average range. Without a report of means and standard deviations it is difficult to interpret the signifigance of the change in scores for the two groups. It is also not possible to know if the two groups were equated on the three subscales of this measure at pretest. The lack of a third control group always raises the question of the contribution of social attention to improved academic performance. Finally, the major criticism is the lack of adequate reporting of the nystagmus duration scores. Two groups were formed based on hyponystagmus but these scores are not given. It is not possible to know what the level of hyponystagmus was in this study. An interrelated issue is that children were subgrouped as having hyponystagmus at pre-test and no measure of nystagmus was obtained at posttest. This is a major difficulty since it is argued that SI therapy facilitates academic progress in children with vestibular dysfunction. To make this argument a pre- vs. post-test change in nystagmus in the therapy group, toward a more normal nystagmus, would be needed. If a positive change did not occur in hyponystagmus, a positive change in another sign of vestibular dysfunction should occur over the time of therapy. This is also important since a third control group was not employed.

In a direct replication of this study, 87 children identified as having learning disabilities and receiving special education in public schools were clinically evaluated by occupational therapists as having moderate problems in sensory integration and being suitable as candidates for SI therapy (Carte et al., 1984). The intellectual level and academic performance of these children are summarized in Table 2. The contrast between the group's intellectual level and low academic performance observed in Table 2 held for the total age range from 6 to 11 years. Additional evaluation established that the sample demonstrated more signs of NBD, such as the tonic neck reflex and poor equilibrium reactions, than developmentally normal children (Morrison, 1982) and performed within the average range on a number of psycholinguistic evaluations (Morrison, 1985). Evidence for perceptual dysfunction and failure to develop automatized visual-scanning techniques was demonstrated through a neuropsychological evaluation (Carte et al., 1984). The children were matched on reading comprehension level, sex, and age and divided into a therapy and no therapy group. All children remained in their regular academic programs but the therapy group received individual SI therapy two to three times a week for a total of 66 sessions over a nine month interval.

SI Therapy: Evaluation and Intervention

There is probably no one accepted detailed definition of SI therapy. It is an evolving practice that will be modified as it is used. Hopefully, evaluation research will contribute to making the change a more rational process. In the Carte et al. (1984) study, conscious effort was made to use only techniques that have evolved from accepted theory and practice (Ayres, 1972a). The evaluation by the occupational therapist focused on four specific areas most related to sensory integration: vestibular, somatosensory, dyspraxia and bilateral integration. Using data from both the SCSIT and PNT assessment, the children were given scores reflecting the degree of dysfunction in each of these four areas. This scoring system ranged from 1, least dysfunctional, to 4, most dysfunctional. Total scores could range from 4, indicating a mild dysfunction in sensory integration, to 16, indicating severe dysfunction. The interscorer reliability for the scoring system proved satisfactory ($r = 0.87$) and the mean score for the total sample was 8.64, SD = 1.87. Based on the evaluation the child was entered into a therapy program. The goals of therapy were relevant to the problems assessed. Examples will be given demonstrating the establishment of a problem during the evaluation and the consequent establishment of treatment goals and the specific procedures used to obtain these goals (Sublett, 1984).

A vestibular processing dysfunction is characterized by hyponystagmus (< 13 sec. total duration), reduced muscle tone, poor ocular-motor pursuit and below average equilibrium reactions. One goal of a therapy program would be to increase muscle tone and prone extension by treatment procedures which appropriately stimulate the vestibular system. For example, the child would be propelled in the supine and prone positions down a ramp on a scooter board. Controlled movement while suspended in a hanging inner tube is also used. A variation of both these techniques to stimulate ocular-motor control is to have the child engaged in throwing objects at targets or grabbing moving objects while in motion. Goals for problems in equilibrium would be to increase equilibrium stability in sitting, kneeling, and standing positions. Techniques used to stimulate muscle tone also are useful for equilibrium reactions. The vestibular system should be stimulated in a variety of planes and directions relative to gravity. Maintaining balance on balance boards, jumping from a platform and landing on inflatables, and a variety of activities that

150

require the child to maintain balance and position in space while moving are useful.

Problems in somatosensory processing are seen in poor body schema and indiscriminate response to tactile stimulation. A goal would be to increase the child's proprioceptive and tactile perception and perception of the body's position in space. Procedures involve the child both actively and passively, and include the child being wrapped in different textured blankets or sandwiched between mats of the same or different weights. Passive or active massage with a vibrator or identifying letters after having their shapes outlined on the child's bare back stimulate tactile awareness. If a child demonstrates tactile defensiveness, appropriate modifications in the level of stimulation must be made.

Poor sequential organization and spatial perception, as well as a poorly developed sense of rhythm and timing, often characterize the child with dyspraxia. A goal would be to expand the child's ability to approach tasks in a sequential rather than disorganized manner. To this end one piece of equipment, such as a platform swing, would be experienced in as many ways as possible. For example, while in a swing the child first sits and pivots, then kneels and pivots, and finally stands and pivots. An elaboration of this procedure is to help the child engage in a series of activities with equipment that he or she arranges. The equipment can be arranged as obstacle courses and rearranged over time by the child. These activities increase the child's spatial awareness and timing. Rhythm and timing can also be improved by gross motor activities such as running and jumping through a series of rubber innertubes or using a jump rope in time with music.

Children with problems in motor planning frequently have problems in bilateral integration. Signs of this problem are ipsilateral use of upper and/or lower extremeties, tendency to avoid crossing midline, and ambidexterity. Therapy would consist of a program to engage the child in activities encouraging the use of both sides of the body in a sequence of simultaneous and reciprocal adaptations demanding midline discrimination. A major goal would be integration of both sides of the body as evidenced by improved eye hand coordination at mid-line and appropriate shifts in body weight for maintenance of equilibrium. The activities used for vestibular dysfunctions can also be modified and used for problems in bilateral integration. Vestibular-proprioceptive activities such as throwing and catching a therapy ball while maintaining balance on a platform swing also stimulate bilateral integration. The ball may be thrown and caught at the midline, and to the left and right in sequence. Poor leg coordination can be addressed by having the child hit targets with one leg or the other or both while moving in a swing. Tasks should require both simultaneous responses, 2 hands and/or 2 feet, and reciprocal responses, one side of the body and then the other.

Obviously many of these procedures address problems in more than one of the evaluated areas and proprioceptive stimulation occurs in most procedures. A therapist would be aware of this and coordinate the activities to reach the overall therapeutic goal. The stimulation of the proprioceptive system will occur with activities that are applied directly to the joint receptors by: (1) joint traction and compression, (2) weight placed on wrists or ankles, while the child or therapist directs joint resistive activity on appropriate equipment, and (3) child directed maintenance of cocontractible resistence. These activities can contribute to the development of body schema, bilateral integration, and muscle tone, as well as increased joint stability.

Treating the Vestibular Processing Dysfunction

This outline of the evaluation procedures used with the 87 children and the treatment procedures used with the therapy group should convey the time and effort needed to provide an individual child an adequate treatment program. Many of the evaluation and intervention procedures evolved directly from the earlier work of the Bobaths (1956, 1971). This work was based on clinical experience with adults and children who demonstrated neuropathology resulting from injury to the brain. Following the medical model, treatment with these patients logically follows diagnosis. The major departure in SI therapy from the treatment methods developed from the clinical experience of physical therapist and physicians (Semans, 1967) has been the focus on the vestibular system. This results in more time being spent in evaluating this system and the use of motion in therapy. Considering the evidence for vestibular processing dysfunctions in LD children, such as hyponystagmus and inadequate equilibrium reactions, this therapeutic emphasis has at least face validity. The vestibular dysfunction interferes indirectly with the learning process. With an adequate trial of SI therapy, sensory integration improves and as a result the interhemispheral capacity of the child's brain increases.

This is the link to improved academic performance since this capacity of the brain is basic to such activities as reading.

> ... normalization of postural mechanisms organized in the midbrain enables better cortical interhemispheral communication, upon which reading must be quite dependent. The postulate is derived from the fact that children with certain types of sensory integrative deficit have difficulty in integrating the sensorimotor functions of the two sides of the body and this problem is ameliorated when postural mechanisms are normalized (Ayres, 1972b).

It is possible that SI therapy could have a positive effect in the children receiving therpy at three different levels (1) sensory integration, (2) perceptual dysfunction, and (3) learning disability. It is also possible that having an effect at the level of sensory integration, it would take time before a positive effect would be detected at either the perceptual or academic performance level. To address these possibilities, the data from the pre and post-test evaluations of the tonic neck reflex, equilibrium reactions, postrotary nystagmus, and visual-motor integration were analyzed for the therapy and no therapy groups (Morrison, 1985). Both groups were equated at pre-test on the four variables and did not differ at post-test evaluations of tonic neck reflexes, equilibrium reactions or visual-motor integration. The reflexes did not demonstrate more inhibition nor did equilibrium reactions improve over the nine month interval. There was no improvement in visual-motor integration in either group. There was a pre- vs. post-test increase in postrotary nystagmus from a below normal duration to a more normal level in both groups. The therapy group did not demonstrate a greater shift over time than did the no-therapy group, although there was a trend in favor of the therapy group.

The analyses of the pre-post test perceptual and academic evaluation were completed on the total group and on a sub-group that was formed on the basis of hyponystagmus at pre-test (Carte et al., 1984). This subgroup was formed since SI therapy effects might be detected more in this sample than the total sample. The results were much the same as the analyses of effects on sensory integration. The exception is that both groups improved over time on both the Target and Underlining tests with no differential effect over time between the two groups. There was no difference between the groups over time on any of the WRAT subscales or in reading comprehension. Over time both groups had a tendency, not quite significant (.058), to improve

153

in reading comprehension. The results were the same for the total sample and the subsample of children with hyponystagmus. There was no age x treatment effect in sensory integration, perceptual dysfunction, or academic achievement.

Conclusion

Lack of significant difference in an evaluation study, using an intervention vs. no intervention control group design, usually does not receive the criticism that is forthcoming when a significant effect is obtained in the intervention group. However, even in the two group design with no results in the intervention group, it is important to have included a range of tests that might reflect the effects of the intervention at different levels. Previous research evaluations of SI therapy have not provided such tests. The lack of effect at the various levels measured in this study provide no support for either the therapy, or the theory of how the therapy might have its therapeutic effects. It does provide support for the existence and clinical importance of neurobehavioral and perceptual dysfunctions.

It is interesting how theory, evaluation, and intervention have been closely associated both in SI therapy (Ayres, 1972a) and perceptual-motor training (Frostig, 1970). This has resulted in a rejection of the total theory, or research results that fail to support the intervention procedures, having the effect of casting doubt on the total effort. It would appear that both interventions have had inconsistent effects. It is also true that greater claims than were warranted have been made for their effectiveness on learning disabilities by theorists who were closely associated and identified with the evaluation and intervention techniques. This is an unfortunate state of affairs and should not prevent us from examining the contribution made by sensory and perceptual dysfunctions in the development and perpetuation of learning disabilities, or evaluating alternative interventions that address these dysfunctions. Future research in intervention should continue to include academic measures as outcome variables, but in the light of the knowledge that these LD children will often have problems in attention and concentration and behavior problems, the design should include appropriate measures of these variables in the outcome battery as well. For example, children in the Carte et al. (1984) study had been evaluated at pre-test as having behavior problems such as hyperactivity and social withdrawal. No post-test measures of these behaviors were obtained. It is possible that the therapy contrib-

154

uted to a reduction in these behaviors independent of the other behaviors evaluated. A result such as this would be of interest to parents, teachers, and clinicians.

A number of studies have provided evidence that vestibular stimulation may reduce hyperactivity in children. Children who had been evaluated by psychiatric criteria and behavior scales as being hyperactive were provided with an interval of rotational vestibular stimulation eight times over a 4-week period. Children served as their own controls in a crossover design and teachers using behavioral scales rated the children as less hyperactive during treatment vs. no treatment conditions. However, the effect was restricted to younger children who were not seen as having undersocialized, aggressive behaviors (Bhatara, Clark, Arnold, Gunsett & Smeltzer, 1981). In a follow-up study controlling for the effects of visual rotary stimulation, children received twice weekly rotational stimulation for eight weeks under conditions of visual input and no visual input. There was a significant effect immediately after treatment and at follow-up one year later. The reduction in hyperactivity was most impressive under the condition of vestibular stimulation alone (Arnold, Clark, Sachs, Jakim & Smithies, 1984). These studies provide a more direct and controlled level of stimulation for the vestibular system. The results suggest the treatment of vestibular processing dysfunction may have more behavior effects than academic effects. However, the studies need to be replicated with an LD sample who demonstrate hyperactivity, with appropriate measures of vestibular dysfunction, such as the PNT, included in the design. The results of these studies also suggest that treatment of vestibular dysfunction may improve academic performance indirectly through a reduction in activity level rather than a major modification in brain function. For example, no improved sensory integration occurs with an underlying improved integration of brain function. What might occur is that hyperactivity is reduced and attention and concentration are more available for perceptual and/or academic learning.

Neither sensory or perceptual integration have received enough attention either in terms of evaluation or treatment. The ability to transfer information from one modality to another has been demonstrated to be a reliable predictor of reading achievement as measured by word knowledge and comprehension. Auditory-visual integration appears to be the system most relevant to reading achievement (Hurley, 1968) while visual-motor integration contributes significantly to reading acquisition until about the 6th grade (Keogh & Smith, 1967).

155

The data suggests that problems in sensory integration contribute to failures to learn, but little research has been done with LD children in which specific intervention techniques were used to improve sensory integration *per se.* In one of the few available studies, letter learning and recognition by young LD children were investigated using visual, tactual, and visual plus tactile training and testing. All children in training and testing conditions using vision, or vision plus touch, made more correct responses than those using touch alone. There was no difference between the vision and vision plus tactual conditions, indicating that the additional input through touch did not positively contribute to acquisition and performance (Baker & Raskin, 1973). These results suggest that visual perception in children of the age range in this study (5.6 to 7.11 years) plays an important role in learning academic subjects. Including touch as a modality may not improve acquisition and performance although it apparently does not interfere with learning. Considering the problems in ocular-motor control in LD children with problems in sensory and perceptual integration, studies of visual-auditory integration under varying conditions of movement may prove useful both in terms of evaluation and intervention. Age should be a controlled variable in such studies since younger children may include more body movement in the reading process than is true of older children.

Finally, LD children with problems in sensory and perceptual integration have an extended period of failure to learn that precedes entry into school. In school the problem may be highlighted and made worse by the academic demands and social pressures that are a part of the child's daily classroom experience. As a result of this lack of positive experience in learning, the child develops low self-esteem and what might be termed phobic reactions to the learning process. Any evaluation or treatment study must include measures of behavior that are sensitive indicators of the possible behavior problems the child may have. These behaviors may not only influence the effect of the intervention but may also change as a result of the intervention. The focus on underlying neurological dysfunctions, or more behaviorally based sensory and perceptual dysfunction, as the major cause of failure to learn fails to recognize that negative motivation also contributes to this process. This motivational aspect of the LD child has not received the attention that is needed. This is particularly true since there is reliable evidence that the long-term prognosis for competent social and emotional development of LD children is poorer compared to developmentally normal children and LD samples show a prevalence of certain psychiatric diagnoses that are not found in children in general (Wenar, 1982, Chap. 9).

An indication of the complex relationship between neuropsychology measures, behavior problems, and academic achievement is found in a study where intervention was provided for the behavior problem (Dean, 1983). Previous research has established that LD children overreact to failure in ways that seriously interfere with learning. In a well controlled study LD children either stayed in their special education class, or were enrolled in a tutorial program, or a behaviorally oriented program that addressed their reactions to failure. In the behavior program, the child's performance on the Halstead-Reitan Battery was used to develop the content of a series of remedial activities. A hierarchy of remedial tasks was then constructed along an approach-avoidance continuum and differential level of reinforcement established which motivated the child to approach more aversive tasks. Pre-post test results were analyzed and produced interesting data on the contribution of motivation to learning in LD children. Few reliable differences occurred in the performance on the neuropsychological battery in any of the children. However, children in the behavior program improved in their area of academic deficit and appropriate classroom behaviors when compared to the other children.

Continued research in the evaluation of LD children will probably establish meaningful subgroups within this population. Hopefully, some of the variables that contribute to making these subgroups different will also suggest suitable methods of intervention. To an important degree this is the major need in this field at this time: the development of objectives and reliable measures whose repeated use over time generates data contributing to predictive and construct validity. This effort may contribute to our knowledge of brain-behavior relationships that has meaning in research and education. As it is now, terms such as "brain dysfunction," "minimal brain damage," and "lack of interhemispheric integration" carry excessive meaning. The terms are both too precise and too vague. They suggest that something specific in the brain is dysfunctional, yet when this dysfunction is linked to a failure to learn, it is found that only behavior can be manipulated, measured or operationally defined. Terms such as NBD, sensory integration, and perceptual dysfunction may be used at times in ways that have excessive meaning but generally these terms have the scientific virtue that they are observable behaviors that can be measured and treated as dependent or independent variables.

This is an advantage to the researcher but is also an advantage to the teacher and practicing clinician who provide diagnostic and intervention services for LD children. Vagueness in concepts can result in evaluation and treatment procedures that are inaccurate, and/or irrelevant, to the presenting problem. Continued application of assessment and treatment procedures, without efforts to assess their clinical value, impedes progress in providing adequate help for the multiple problems endured by LD children and their families.

The child demonstrating neurobehavioral and perceptual dysfunctions should receive intervention during the period of early academic experience. Early screening programs such as SEARCH and intervention programs such as TEACH (Silver & Hagen, 1981) may prove effective if they are provided at this time. Dealing directly with the perceptual dysfunction, and helping the child develop automatized perceptual processing skills, may prevent early failure as well as the early development of behavior problems. As was noted earlier, children receiving this intervention did not demonstrate hyperactive behavior during the second year of school. Intervention for the vestibular problems, such as controlled vestibular stimulation and specific interventions to develop visual-motor and visual-auditory integration, should be provided. Older LD children with neurobehavioral and perceptual dysfunctions present a more complicated problem. Certainly, treatment of the vestibular processing problems should be provided and this could be part of the child's curriculum. However, it could be that in older children these particular dysfunctions may have to be treated medically rather than educationally. Although the initial claims for the effectiveness of medication for vestibular processing dysfunctions (Levinson, 1983) lack an acceptable research base, it is premature to reject this approach. It is also an area that can be examined by research. The older NBD child of eight or nine who becomes identified as having a learning disability will also have a high probability of showing a number of behavior problems as well as an aversion to learning. Frequently, these children have adequate auditory and psycholinguistic skills, but are falling behind their peers in academic tasks such as reading. Although efforts should be made to deal with their perceptual and cognitive weaknesses, it may be beneficial to place more emphasis on their strengths. Approaching these children with teaching strategies which take advantage of their preferred modality and circumvent the processing weakness, increases the probability of success and reduces the chances of negative emotional reactions.

158

Bibliography

Achenbach, J., & Lewis, M. (1971). A proposed model for clinical research and its application to encopresis and enuresis. *Journal of the American Academy of Child Psychiatry, 10,* 535–554.

Allport, F.H. (1955). *Theories of perception and the concept of structure.* New York: John Wiley & Sons.

Amante, D., Van Houten, V., Grieve, J., Bader, C., & Margules, P. (1977). Neuropsychological deficit, ethnicity and socioeconomic status. *Journal of Consulting and Clinical Psychology, 4,* 524–535.

American Psychiatric Association (1980). *Diagnositic and Statistical Manual of Mental Disorders* (3rd ed.). Washington, DC: Author.

Arnold, L. (1983). Review of: "A solution to the riddle of dyslexia" by Levinson, H. *Journal of the American Academy of Child Psychiatry, 5,* 503–505.

Arnold, L., Barnebey, N., McManus, J., Smeltzer, D., Conrad, A., Winer, G., & Desgranges, L. (1977). Prevention by specific perceptual remediation for vulnerable first-graders: Controlled study and follow-up of lasting effects. *Archives of General Psychiatry, 34,* 1279–1294.

Arnold, L., Clark, D., Sach, L., Jakim, S., & Smithies, C. (1984). *Vestibular and visual rotation stimulation as treatment for attention deficit and hyperactivity.* Unpublished manuscript, Department of Psychiatry, Ohio State University.

Arnold, L., Smeltzer, D., & Barnebey, N. (1981). Specific perceptual remediation: Effects related to sex. IQ, and parental occupational status. *Psychological Reports, 49,* 198.

Ayres, J. (1961). Development of the body scheme in children. *American Journal of Occupational Therapy, 3,* 99–128.

Ayres, J. (1969). Deficits in sensory integration in educational handicapped children. *Journal of Learning Disabilities, 2,* 160–168.

Ayres, J. (1972a). *Sensory integration and learning disorders.* Los Angeles: Western Psychological Services.

Ayres, J. (1972b). Improving academic scores through sensory integration. *Journal of Learning Disabilities, 5,* 338–343.

Ayres, J. (1975). *Southern California Postrotary Nystagmus Test Manual.* Los Angeles: Western Psychological Services.

Ayres, J. (1976). *Interpreting the Southern California Sensory Integration Tests.* Los Angeles: Western Psychological Services.

Ayres, J. (1978). Learning disabilities and the vestibular system. *Journal of Learning Disabilities, 1,* 30–41.

Ayres, J. (1980). *Southern California Sensory Integration Test.* Los Angeles: Western Psychological Services.

Baker, G., & Raskin, L. (1973). Sensory integration in the learning disabled. *Journal of Learning Disabilities, 10,* 53–57.

Bandura, A. (1969). *Principles of behavior modification.* New York, NY: Holt, Rinehart & Winston.

Barsch, R. (1968). *Achieving perceptual-motor efficiency: A space oriented approach to learning. Vol. 1.* Seattle, WA: Special Child Publications.

Beery, K.E. (1982). *Developmental Test of Visual-Motor Integration.* Cleveland, OH: Modern Curriculum Press.

Bender, L. (1938). A visual-motor gestalt test and its clinical use. *American Orthopsychiatric Association Research Monograph,* No. 3.

Bender, L., & Faretra (1972). The relationship between childhood schizophrenia and adult schizophrenia. In A. Kaplan (Ed.), *Genetic factors in schizophrenia.* Springfield, IL: Charles C. Thomas.

Benton, A.L. (1955). Right-left discrimination and finger-localization in defective children. *Archives of Neurology and Psychiatry, 74,* 583–589.

Berman, A., & Siegel, A. (1976). A neurological approach to the etiology, prevention, and treatment of juvenile delinquency. In A. Davis (Ed.), *Child personality and psychopathology: Current topics.* New York, NY: Wiley.

Bhatara, V., Clark, D., Arnold, L., Gunsett, R., & Smeltzer, D. (1981). Hyperkinesis treated by vestibular stimulation: An exploratory study. *Biological Psychiatry, 3,* 269–279.

Bijou, S.W., & Baer, D. (1960). The laboratory experimental study of child behavior. In Mussen, P. (Ed.), *Handbook of research methods in child development.* New York: John Wiley & Sons.

Birch, H.G., & Belmont, L. (1964). Auditory-visual integration in normal and retarded readers. *American Journal of Orthopsychiatry, 34,* 852–861.

Bobath, B. (1971). *Abnormal postural reflex activity caused by brain lesions.* London: William Heinemann Medical Books.

Bobath, K., & Bobath, B. (1956). The diagnosis of cerebral palsy in infancy. *Archives of the Disabled Child, 31,* 408–414.

Bobath, B., & Bobath, K. (1975). *Motor development in the different types of cerebral palsy.* London: William Heineman Medical Books.

Boder, E., & Jarrico, S. (1982). *Boder Test of Reading-Spelling Patterns: A diagnostic test for subtypes of reading disability.* New York: Grune & Stratton.

Bogacz, L., Mendilaharsu, C., & Mendelaharsu, S.A. (1974). Electro-oculographic abnormalities during pursuit movements in developmental dyslexia. *Electroencephalography and Clinical Neurophysiology, 36,* 651–656.

Bouma, H., & Legein, C.P. (1977). Foveal and parafoveal recognition of letters and words by dyslexics and average readers. *Neuropsychologia, 15,* 69–80.

Boverman, D.M. (1964). Generality and behavior correlates of cognitive styles. *Journal of Consulting Psychology, 28,* 487–500.

Boverman, D., Boverman, I., & Klaiber, E. (1966). The ability to automatic and the automatization cognitive style: A validation study. *Journal of Perceptual Motor Skills, 2,* 419–437.

Bruininks, R.H. (1977). *Bruininks-Oseretsky Test of Motor Proficiency manual.* Circle Pines, MN: American Guidance Service.

160

Bruininks, V., & Bruininks, R. (1977). Motor proficiency of learning disabled and nondisabled students. *Perceptual and Motor Skills, 44,* 1131–1137.

Capute, A. Accardo, P., Vining, P., Rubenstein, J., & Harryman, S. (1978). *Primitive Reflex Profile,* Baltimore: University Park Press.

Carte, E., Morrison, D., Sublett, J., Uemura, A., & Setrakian, W. (1984). Sensory integration therapy: A trial of a specific neurodevelopmental therapy for the remediation of learning disabilities. *Developmental and Behavioral Pediatrics, 4,* 189–194.

Cermak, S., & Ayres, J. (1984). Crossing the body midline in learning disabled and normal children. *American Journal of Occupational Therapy, 1,* 35–39.

Cermak, S., Quintero, E., & Cohen, P. (1980). Developmental age trends in crossing the body midline in normal children. *American Journal of Occupational Therapy 5,* 313–319.

Conners, C.K. (1970). "Parents' questionnaire" in symptom patterns in hyperkinetic, neurotic, and normal children. *Child Development, 41,* 667–682.

Cullinan, D., Epstein, M., & Lloyd J. (1983). *Behavior disorders of childhood and adolescents.* Englewood Cliffs, NJ: Prentice-Hall.

Dean, R.S. (1983). *Integrating neuropsychological and emotional variables in the treatment of children's learning disorders.* Paper presented at the American Psychological Association Convention, August, Anaheim, CA.

DeGangi, G.A. (1982). The relationship of vestibular responses and developmental functions in high risk infants. *Physical and Occupational Therapy in Pediatrics, 2,* 35–48.

DeGangi, G., Beck, R., & Larsen, L. (1981). The measurement of vestibular-based functions in pre-school children. *American Journal of Occupational Therapy, 35,* 443–450.

Denkla, M., & Rudel, R. (1976). Rapid automized naming (R.A.N.): Dyslexia differentiated from other learning disabilities. *Neuropsychologia, 14,* 471–479.

Denny, D.R. (1974). Relationship of three cognitive style dimensions to elementary reading abilities. *Journal of Educational Psychology, 66,* 702–709.

deQuiros, J. (1976). Diagnosis of vestibular disorders in the learning disabled. *Journal of Learning Disabilities, 9,* 50–57.

deQuiros, J., & Scharger, O. (1979). *Neuropsychological fundamentals in learning disabilities.* Novato, CA: Academic Therapy Publications.

Deutsch, M., Katz, I., & Jensen, A. (1968). *Social class, race, and psychological development.* New York: Holt, Rinehart & Winston.

Dietz, J., Siegner, & C., Crowe, T. (1981). The Southern California Postrotary Nystagmus Test: Test-rest reliability for pre-school children. *American Journal of Occupational Therapy, 1,* 166–175.

Dix, M.R. (1980). The mechanism and clinical significace of optokinetic nystagmus. *The Journal of Laryngology and Otology, 94,* 845–864.

Doehring, D.G. (1968). *Patterns of impairments in specific reading disability.* Bloomington: Indiana University Press.

Donoghue, E., Kirman, B., Bullmore, G., Laban, D., & Abbas, K. (1970). Some factors affecting age of walking in a mentally retarded population. *Developmental Medicine and Child Neurology, 12,* 781–792.

161

Eakin, S., & Douglas, V. (1971). Automatization and oral reading problems in children. *Journal of Learning Disabilities, 1*, 31–38.

Easton, T.A. (1972). On the normal use of reflexes. *American Scientist, 60*, 591–599.

Edelborck, C., & Achenbach, T. (1980). A typology of child behavior profile patterns: Distribution and correlates for disturbed children aged 6–16. *Journal of Abnormal Child Psychology, 8*, 441–470.

Feagan, L. (1983). A current view of learning disability. *Journal of Pediatrics, 102*, 487–492.

Finocchario, A. (1974). Behavioral characteristics of learning disabled children. *American Journal of Occupational Therapy, 28*, 30–35.

Fraiberg, S. (1977). *Insights from the blind: Comparative studies of blind and sighted infants.* New York: Basic Books.

Frank, J., & Levinson, H. (1976). Compensatory mechanisms in CV dysfunction, dymetric dyslexia and dyspraxia. *Academic Therapy, 1*, 5–25.

Frank, J., & Levinson, H. (1976b) Seasickness mechanisms and medication in dysmetric dyslexia and dyspraxia. *Academic Therapy, 2*, 133–151.

Freides, D., Barbati, J., van Kampen.-Horowitz, L., Sprehn, G., Iversen, C., Silver, J., & Woodward, R. (1980). Blind evaluation of body reflexes and motor skills in learning disability. *Journal of Autism and Developmental Disorders, 2*, 159–171.

Friedlander, S., Pothier, P., Morrison, D., & Herman, L. (1982). The role of neurological-developmental delay in childhood psychopathology. *American Journal of Orthopsychiatry, 52*, 102–108.

Frostige, M. (1970). *Movement education: Theory and practice.* Chicago: Follet Educational Corp.

Gaddes, W.H. (1980). *Learning disabilities and brain function: A neuropsychological approach.* New York: Springer-Verlag.

Gesell, A. (1940). *The first five years of life.* New York: Harper and Row.

Golden, C. (1982). The Luria-Nebraska Children's Battery: Theory and formulation. In G. Hynd & J. Obrzut (Eds.), *Neuropsychological assessment of the school-age child.* New York: Grune & Stratton.

Golden, C.J., & Anderson, S. (1979). *Learning disability and brain dysfunction.* Springfield, IL: Charles C. Thomas.

Goody, W., & Reingold, W. (1952). Some aspects of human orientation in space: Sensation and movement. *Brain, 75*, 472–509.

Gregory-Flock, J., & Yerxa, E. (1983). Standardization of the prone extension postural test on children age 4 through 8. *American Journal of Occupational Therapy, 3*, 187–195.

Head, J. (1912). Sensory-disturbances from cerebral lesions. *Brain, 34*, 102–254.

Head, J. (1955). *Aphasia and kindred disorders of speech. Vol. 1.* New York: Cambridge University Press.

Hebb, D.O. (1949). *The organization of behavior.* New York: John Wiley & Sons.

Held, R. (1973). Plasticity in sensory-motor systems. In *Nature and nurture of behavior.* San Francisco, CA: W.H. Freeman and Company.

Hellebrandt, F., Houtz, S.J., & Krikonan, A. (1956). Tonic neck reflexes in exercises of stress in man. *American Journal of Physical Medicine, 35,* 144–154.

Henker, B., & Whalen, C.K. (1985). The many messages of medication: Hyperactive children's perceptions and attributions. In J: Antrobus (Ed.), *The ecosystem of the "sick child."* San Francisco, CA: Jossey-Bass.

Hoffer, W. (1950). Development of the body ego. *Psychoanalytic Study of the Child, 4,* 18–23.

Hunt, J. McV. (1964). The psychological basis for using pre-school enrichment as an antidote for cultural deprivation. *Merrill-Palmer Quarterly of Behavior and Development, 10,* 209.

Hurley, O. (1968). Perceptual integration and reading problem. *Exceptional Children,* Nov., 207–215.

Hynd, G., & Obrzut, J. (1981). *Neuropsychological assessment and the school-age child.* New York: Grune & Stratton.

Ikai, M. (1950). Tonic neck reflex in normal person. *Japanese Journal of Physiology, 1,* 118–124.

Illingworth, R.S. (1968). Delayed motor development. *Pediatric Clinics of North America, 15,* 569–580.

Jastek, D.E. (1978). *The Wide Range Achievement Test.* Wilmington, DE: D.E. Jastek Associates, Inc.

Jenkins, J., & Sells, C. (1984). Physical and occupational therapy: Effects related to treatment frequency and motor delay. *Journal of Learning Disabilities, 2,* 89–95.

Jensen, P., Friedlander, S., Traylor, J., Morrison, D., & Philips, I. (1983). *Reliability and agreement of reports of children's symptoms.* Paper presented at the American Academy of Child Psychiatry Convention, August, San Francisco, CA.

Jung-Finacchario, A. (1974). Behavior characteristics in learning disabled children with postural reflex dysfunction. *American Journal of Occupational Therapy, 28,* 18–22.

Karniski, W., Levine, M., Clarke, S., Palfrey, J., & Meltzer, L. (1982). A study of neurodevelopmental findings in early adolescent delinquents. *Journal of Adolescent Health Care, 3,* 151–159.

Kaufman, A., & Kaufman, N. (1983. *Kaufman Assessment Battery for Children.* Circle Pines, MN: American Guidance Service.

Kavale, D., & Mattson, P.D. (1983). "One jumped off the balance beam": Meta-analysis of perceptual-motor training. *Journal of Learning Disabilities, 16,* 165–173.

Kazdin, A., French, N., Unis, A., & Esveldt-Dawson, R. (1983). Assessment of childhood depression: Correspondence of child and parent ratings. *Journal of the American Academy of Child Psychiatry, 22,* 157–164.

Keating, N. (1979). A comparison of duration of nystagmus as measured by the Southern California Postrotary Nystagmus Test and electronystagmography. *The American Journal of Occupational Therapy, 2,* 92–97.

Keogh, B.K., & Margolis, J. (1976). Learn to labor and wait: Attentional problems in children with learning disorders. *Journal of Learning Disabilities, 9,* 18–28.

Keogh, B. & Smith, C. (1967). Visuo-motor ability for school prediction: A seven year study. *Perceptual Motor Skills, 25,* 101–110.

Kephart, N.C. (1960). *The slow learner in the classroom.* Columbus, OH: Charles E. Merrill.

Khanna, J.L. (1973). *Brain damage and mental retardation.* Springfield, IL: Charles C. Thomas.

Kimball, J.G. (1981). Normative comparison of the Southern California Post-rotary Nystagmus Test: Los Angeles vs. Syracuse data. *American Journal of Occupational Therapy, 35,* 21–25.

Kinsbourne, M. (1985). Monitoring how disabled learners think with laterality tests. In S. Ceci (Ed.), *Handbook of cognitive, social and neuropsychological aspects of learning disabilities.* New Jersey: Lawrence Erlbaum Associates.

Knights, R.M., & Bakker, D. (1980). *Treatment of hyperactive and learning disordered children.* Baltimore, MD: University Park Press.

Knights, R.M., & Norwood, J. (1980). *A Neurological Test Battery for Children: Examiner's manual.* Ottawa, Canada: Knights Psychological Consultants.

Knopf, I.J. (1983). *Childhood psychpathology: A developmental approach.* New Jersey: Prentice-Hall.

Kornhuber, V. (1974). *The vestibular system, Part 2: Psychophysics and applied aspects, general interpretations.* New York: Springer-Verlag.

Kovacs, M., & Beck, A. (1977). An empirical clinical approach toward a definition of childhood depression. In J. Schulterbrandt & A. Raskin (Eds.), *Depression in childhood: Diagnosis, treatment and conceptual models.* New York: Raven Press.

LaBerge, D., & Samuels, S.J. (1974). Toward a theory of automatic information processing in reading. *Cognitive Psychology, 6,* 293–323.

Larrabee, M. (1982). Reexamination of a plea for mutlivariate analyses. *Journal of Counseling Psychology, 2,* 180–188.

Lassek, A.M. (1957). *The human brain from primitive to modern.* Springfield: IL: Charles C. Thomas.

Leary, M.R., & Altmaier, E.M. (1980). Type 1 error in counseling research: A plea for mutlivariate analyses. *Journal of Counseling Psychology, 27,* 611–615.

Leisman, G. (Ed.) (1975). *Basic visual processes and learning disability.* Springfield, IL: Charles C. Thomas.

Leisman, G., & Schwartz, J. (1976). Ocular-motor variables in reading disorders. In R.M. Knights & D. Bakker (Eds.), *The neuropsychology of learning disorders.* Baltimore, MD: University Park Press.

Lere, R.J. (1981). An open letter to an occupational therapist. *Journal of Learning Disabilities, 14,* 3–4.

Lerner, J. (1981). *Learning disabilities.* Boston: Houghton Mifflin.

Leseure, N. (1968). L'organisation due regard chez des enfants d'age scolaire, lectuers normaux et dyslexiques. *Revue de Neuropsychiatrie Infantiel et D'Hygiene Mentale de L'Enfance, 4,* 323–349.

Levinson, H. (1983). *A solution to the riddle of dyslexia.* New York: Springer-Verlag.

Lewis, D.O., Shanok, S., Balla, D., & Bard, B. (1980). Psychiatric correlates of severe reading disabilities in an incarcerated delinquent population. *Journal of the American Academy of Child Psychiatry, 19,* 611–622.

Lindsay, G.A., & Wedell, K. (1982). The early identification of educationally "at-risk" children revisited. *Journal of Learning Disabilities, 15,* 212–217.

Loney, J., & Halmi, K. (1980). Clinical treatment research: Its design, execution, analysis and interpretation. *Biological Psychiatry, 1,* 147–156.

Luria, A.R. (1966). *Higher cortical functions in man.* New York: Basic Books.

Luria, A.R. (1973). *The working brain.* New York: Basic Books.

Magnus, R. (1926). Physiology of posture. *Lancet, 2,* 531–536 & 585–588.

Marcel, T., & Rajan, P. (1975). Lateral specialization for recognition of words and faces in good and poor readers. *Neuropsychologia, 13,* 489–497.

Mann, L.S. (1970). Perceptual training: Misdirections and redirections. *American Journal of Orthopsychiatry, 1,* 30–38.

Marx, M.H. (1951). *Psychological theory.* New York: The Macmillan Company.

Mathog, R. (1972). Testing of the vestibular system by sinusodal angular acceleration. *Acta Otolaryngologia, 74,* 96–103.

McKeever, W., & Van Devente, A. (1975). Dyslexic adolescents: Evidence of imparied visual and auditory language processing skills associated with normal lateralization and visual responsivity. *Cortex, 11,* 361–378.

Milani-Comparetti, A., & Gidoni, E.A. (1967). Pattern analysis of motor development and its disorders. *Developmental Medicine and Child Neurology, 9,* 625–630.

Mitchell, R.G. (1960). The Moro reflex. *Cerebral Palsy Bulletin, 2,* 135–141.

Molnar, G.E. (1978). Analysis of motor disorder in retarded infants and young children. *American Journal of Mental Deficiency, 3,* 213–222.

Montgomery, P., & Capps, M. (1980). Effects of arousal on the nystagmus response of normal children. *Physical and Occupational Therapy in Pediatrics, 1,* 17–29.

Montgomery, P., & Rodel, D. (1982). Effect of state on nystagmus duration on the Southern California Postrotary Nystagmus Test. *American Journal of Occupational Therapy, 36,* 177–182.

Morrison, D. (1982). *Neurodevelopmental delay in normal, neurologically handicapped and dyslexic children.* Paper presented at the American Psychological Association Convention, September, Washington, D.C.

Morrison, D. (1985). *The effects of sensory integration therapy on vestibular processing dysfunction.* Paper presented at the Western Psychological Association Convention, April, San Jose, CA.

Morrison, D., Pothier, P., & Horr, K. (1978). *Sensory-motor dysfunction and therapy in infancy in early childhood.* Springfield, IL: Charles C. Thomas.

Morrison, D., & Sublett, J. (1983). Reliability of the Southern California Postrotary Nystagmus Test with learning disabled children. *American Journal of Occupational Therapy, 37,* 694–697.

165

Naylor, H. (1980). Reading disability and lateral assymetry: An information-processing analysis. *Psychological Bulletin, 3,* 531–545.

Neligan, G.E., & Prudham, D. (1969). Potential value of four early developmental milestones in screening children for increase risk of later retardation. *Developmental Medicine & Child Neurology, 11,* 423–431.

Nobak, C., & Demarest, R. (1975). *The human nervous system: Basic principles of neuropshysiology* (2nd ed.). New York: McGraw-Hill.

Offord, D., Poushinsky, M., & Sullivan, D. (1978). School performance, IQ, and deliquency. *British Journal of Criminology, 18,* 110–127.

Ornitz, E. (1970). Vestibular dysfunction in schizophrenia and childhood autism. *Comprehensive Psychiatry, 11,* 159–173.

Orton, S.T. (1937). *Reading, writing, and speech problems in children.* New York: W.H. Norton.

Ottenbacher, K. (1980). Excessive postrotary nystagmus duration in learning disabled children. *American Journal of Occupational Therapy, 1,* 40–44.

Ottenbacher, K. (1982). Sensory integration therapy: Affect or effect. *American Journal of Occupational Therapy, 9,* 571–578.

Ottenbacher, K., Short, M., & Watson, P. (1979). Nystagmus duration changes of learning disabled childrend during sensory integrative therapy. *Perceptual and Motor Skills, 48,* 1159–1164.

Ottenbacher, K., Watson, P., & Short, M. (1979). Association between nystagmus hyporesponsivity and behavioral problems in learning disabled children. *American Journal of Occupational Therapy, 33,* 317–322.

Overall, J.E., & Klett, C. (1972). *Applied multivariate analysis.* New York: McGraw-Hill.

Paine, R.S. (1964). The evolution of infantile postural reflexes in the presence of chronic brain syndromes. *Developmental Medicine and Child Neurology, 6,* 345–361.

Parker, D.E. (1980). The vestibular apparatus. *Scientific American, 5,* 118–135.

Parmenter, C.L. (1975). The asymmetrical tonic neck reflex in normal first and third grade children. *American Journal of Occupational Therapy, 29,* 463–468.

Parr, C., Routh, D.K., & Byrd, M. (1974). A developmental study of the asymmetrical tonic neck reflex *Developmental Medicine and Child Neurology, 16,* 329–335.

Parson, O.A., & Prigatano, G. (1978). Methodological considerations in clinical neuropsychological research. *Journal of Consulting and Clinical Psychology, 46,* 608–619.

Pavlidis, G. (1981). Sequencing, eye movements and the early objective diagnosis of dyslexia. In G. Pavlidis & T. Miles (Eds.), *Dyslexia research and its application to education.* New York: John Wiley & Sons.

Pelham, W., & Ross, A. (1977). Selective attention in children with reading problems: A developmental study of incidental learning. *Journal of Abnormal Child Psychology, 1,* 1–8.

Petri, J., & Anderson, M. (1980). Eye and head movements in reading disabled and normal children. *American Journal of Occupational Therapy, 12,* 801–808.

Piaget, J. (1952). *The origins of intelligence in children.* New York: International University Press.

Piaget, J. (1954). *The construction of reality in the child.* New York: Basic Books.

Piaget, J. (1962). *Play, dreams and imitation in childhood.* New York: Norton & Company.

Piaget, J. (1971). *Biology and knowledge.* Chicago: University of Chicago.

Piaget, J. (1979). *The child's conception of the world.* Totowa, NJ: Littlefield-Adams & Company.

Pothier, P., Friedlander, S., Morrison, D., & Herman, L. (1983). Procedure for assessment of neurodevelopmental delay in young children. *Child: Health, Care & Development, 9,* 73–83.

Poynter, H. Schor, C., Haynes, H., & Hirsch, J. (1982). Oculomotor function in reading disability. *American Journal of Optometry & Psychological Optics, 2,* 116–127.

Price, A. (1977). Nationally speaking: Sensory integration therapy in occupational therapy. *American Journal of Occupational Therapy, 31,* 287–289.

Punwar, A. (1982). Expanded normative data: Southern California Postrotary Nystagmus test. *American Journal of Occupational Therapy, 36,* 183–187.

Reynolds, C. (1983). *Clinical acumen but psychometric naivete in neuropsychological research and practice.* Paper presented American Psychological Association Meeting, August, Anaheim, California.

Reitan, R., & Davison, L. (1974). *Clinical neuropsychology: Current status and applications.* Washington, DC: V.H. Winston and Sons.

Rider, B.A. (1972). Relationship of postural reflexes to learning disabilities. *American Journal of Occupational Therapy, 26,* 239–243.

Rider, B.A. (1973). Perceptual-motor dysfunction in emotionally disturbed children. *American Journal of Occupational Therapy, 27,* 316–320.

Rosinski, R.R. (1977). *The development of visual-perception.* Santa Monica, CA: Goodyear Publishing.

Ross, A.O. (1973). Conceptual issues in the evaluation of brain damage. In J.L. Khanna (Ed.), *Brain damage and mental retardation.* Springfield, IL: Charles C. Thomas.

Rourke, B., & Finlayson, M. (1978). Neuropsychological significance of variation in patterns of academic performance, verbal and visual-spatial abilities. *Journal of Abnormal Child Psychology, 6,* 121–133.

Rourke, B.P., & Gates, R. (1981). Neuropsychological research and school psychology. In G. Hynd & J. Obrzut (Ed.), *Assessment of the school-age child.* New York: Grune & Stratton.

Rourke, B., & Orr, R. (1977). Prediction of the reading and spelling performance of normal and retarded readers: A four-year follow-up. *Journal of Abnormal Child Psychology, 1,* 9–20.

Royeen, C.B. (1980). Factors affecting test-retest reliability of the Southern California Postrotary Nystagmus Test. *American Journal of Occupational Therapy, 1,* 37–39.

Rutter, M. (1977). Brain damage syndromes in childhood: Concepts and findings. *Journal of Child Psychology and Psychiatry, 18,* 1–21.

167

Rutter, M. (1982). Syndromes attributed to "minimal brain dysfunction" in childhood. *American Journal of Psychiatry, 1*, 21–31.

Rutter, M. (Ed.) (1984). *Developmental neuropsychiatry.* New York: The Guilford Press.

Rutter, M., Tizard, J., & Whitmore, K. (Eds.) (1970). *Education, health and behavior.* London: Longmans.

Sanford, H.N. (1933). The Moro reflex in the newborn. *American Journal of the Disabled Child, 46*, 337–340.

Saphier, J. (1973). The relation of perceptual-motor skills to learning an school success. *Journal of Learning Disabilities, 9*, 56–63.

Satz, P., & Friel, J. (1974). Some predictive antecedents of specific learning disability: A preliminary two-year follow-up. *Journal of Learning Disability, 7*, 437–444.

Satz, P., Friel, J., & Goebel, R. (1975). Some predictive antecendents of specific reading disability: A three year follow-up. *Bulletin of the Orton Society, 25*, 91–110.

Schlesinger, H., & Meadow, K. (1972). *Sound and Sign.* Berkeley, CA: University of California Press.

Selz, M. (1981). Halstead-Reitan Neuropsychological Test Batteries for Children. In G. Hynd & J. Obrzut (Eds.), *Neuropsychological assessment of the school-age child.* New York: Grune & Stratton.

Selz, M., & Reitan, R. (1979). Rules for neuropsychogical diagnosis: Classification of brain functions in older children. *Journal of Consulting and Clinical Psychology, 47*, 258–264.

Semans, S. (1967). The Bobath concept in treatment of neurological disorders. *American Journal of Physical Medicine, 46*, 732–785.

Senf, G., & Freundl, P. (1971). Memory and attention factors in specific learning disabilities. *Journal of Learning Disabilities, 2*, 36–48.

Sherick, I., Greeniman, G., & Legg, C. (1976). Some comments on the significance and development of midline behavior during infancy. *Child Psychiatry and Human Development, 6*, 170–183.

Sherrington, C. (1961). *The integrative action of the nervous system.* New Haven: Yale University Press.

Sieg, K., & Shuster, J. (1979). Comparison of three positions for evaluating the asymmetrical tonic neck reflex. *American Journal of Occupational Therapy, 33*, 311–316.

Siegner, C., Crowe, T., & Deitz, J. (1982). Interrater reliability of the Southern California Postrotary Nystagmus Test. *Physical and Occupational Therapy in Pediatrics, 2*, 83–91.

Silver, A.A. (1952). Postural righting responses in children. *Journal of Pediatrics, 41*, 493–498.

Silver, A.A., & Hagin, R. (1981). *SEARCH and TEACH.* New York: Walker Educational Book Corporation.

Silver, L.B. (1976). The playroom diagnostic evaluation of children with neurologically based learning disabilities. *Journal of the American Academy of Child Psychiatry, 15*, 240–256.

Sines, J.O. (1964). Actuarial methods as appropriate strategy for the validation of diagnostic tests. *Psychological Review, 71*, 517–523.

Spears, W., & Hohle, R. (1967). Sensory and perceptual development in infants. In Y. Brackbill (Ed.), *Infancy and early childhood.* New York: Free Press.

Spector, M. (1967). *Dizziness and vertigo.* New York: Grune & Stratton.

Speery, R.W. (1964). The great cerebral commissure. *Scientific American, 210,* 42–53.

Spitz, R. (1965). *The first year of life.* New York: International Universities Press.

Spivack, J., & Swift, M. (1967). *Devereaux Elementary School Behavior Rating Scale.* Devon, PA: The Devereus Foundation.

Stilwell, J.M. (1981). Relationship between development of the body-righting reaction and manual midline crossing behavior in the learning disabled. *American Journal of Occupational Therapy, 6,* 391–398.

Sublett, J. (1984). *Manual for Sensory Integration Therapy.* Kentfield, CA: The CHILD Center.

Sweeney, J., & Rourke, B. (1978). Neuropsychological significance of phonetically accurate and phonetically inaccurate spelling errors in younger and older retarded spellers. *Brain and Language, 6,* 212–225.

Tallal, P., & Piercy, M. (1973). Defects of non-verbal auditory perception in children with developmental asphasia. *Nature, 241,* 468–469.

Tarnapol, L. (1970). Deliquency and minimal brain dysfunction. *Journal of Learning Disabilities, 3,* 200–207.

Tarver, S.G., & Hallahan, D. (1974). Attention deficits in children with learning disabilities: A review. *Journal of Learning Disabilities, 7,* 560–572.

Tibbling, L. (1969). The rotary nystagmus response in children. *Acta Otolaryngol, 68.* 459–467.

Twitchell, T. (1965a). Attitudinal reflexes. *Journal of the American Physical Therapy Association, 45,* 411–418.

Twitchell, T. (1965b). Normal motor development. *Journal of the American Physical Therapy Association, 45,* 419–473.

Vander Laan, F., & Oosterveld, W. (1974). Age and vestibular function. *Aerospace Medicine, 45,* 540–547.

Vasella, F., & Karlsson, B. (1962). Asymmetric tonic neck reflex. *Developmental Medicine and Child Neurology, 4,* 363–369.

Vellutino, F. (1977). Alternative conceptualizations of dyslexia: Evidence in support of a verbal deficit hypothesis. *Harvard Educational Review, 47,* 334–354.

Velluntino, F., Steger, B., Moyer, S., Harding, C., & Niles, J. (1970). Has the perceptual deficit hypothesis led us astray? *Journal of Learning Disabilities, 6,* 375–385.

Wachs, T. (1976). Utilization of a Piagetian approach in the investigation of early experience effects. *Merrill-Palmer Quarterly, 1,* 11–31.

Walters, E. (1967). Interaction of the body and its segments. *American Journal of Physical Medicine. 1,* 280–289.

Waterland, J. (1967). Willed movement. *American Journal of Physical Medicine, 46,* 266–278.

Watson, J.B. (1962). *Behaviorism.* Chicago: University of Chicago Press.

Wechler, D. (1974). *Manual for the Wechsler Intelligence Scale for Children – Revised.* New York: The Psychological Corporation.

Wenar, C. (1982). *Psychopathology from infancy through adolescense.* New York: Random House.

Werner, H., & Wapner, S. (1949). Sensory-tonic field theory of perception. *Journal of Personality, 18,* 88–107.

Wigglesworth, R. (1961). Minimal cerebral palsy. *Cerebral Palsy Bulletin, 3,* 293–295.

Witkins, H.A., Dyk, R., Faterson, H,F. Goodenough, D., & Karp, S. (1962). *Psychological Differentiation.* New York: John Wiley & Sons.

Zapella, M., Foley, J., & Cookson, M. (1964). The placing and supporting reaction in mental deficiency. *Journal of Mental Deficiency Research, 8,* 1–5.

Author Index

Sherick, I., 61, 124
Sherrington, C., 12
Sieg, K., 53, 57, 100
Silver, A.A., 51, 103, 127, 156
Silver, L.B., 123, 140

Spears, W., 142

Spector, M., 78
Spitz, R., 123
Spivack, J., 131
Stilwell, J.M., 99, 100
Sublett, J., 148
Sweeney, J., 109

Tallal, P., 121
Tarnapol, L., 126

Tarver, S.G., 115
Tibbling, L., 75
Twitchell, T., 12, 13

VanderLaan, F., 81
Vasella, F., 50
Vellutino, F., 27, 91, 139

Walters, E., 12
Waterland, J., 12
Watson, J.B., 12
Wechler, D., 31, 112
Wenar, C., 155
Werner, H., 22, 29
Wigglesworth, R., 15
Witkins, H.A., 128, 129

Zapella, M., 15, 60

Subject Index

Palmer grasp reflex, 12
Perception, 20, 29
Perceptual-motor therapy, 27, 34, 142
Postural reflexs, 13, 15, 63, 95
Preoperational thought, 5, 95
Primitive reflexs, 11, 13, 16
Primitive Reflex and Postural Adjustment Procedure (PRPA), 58, 137
Prone extension posture, 66, 68
Proprioceptive, 25, 150
Protective extension, 69, 71
Psycholinguistic deficit, 139

Rapid Automatized Naming Test (RAN), 117
Reading retardation, 93, 113, 127
Righting reactions, 16
Romberg's test, 70

Saccades, 94
Saccule, 69, 78
Sampling issues, 36, 99-101, 131, 142
Schizophrenic children, 125
Semicircular canals, 77
Sensorimotor intelligence, 22, 29
Sensory integration, 22, 90
    Assessment, 34, 41
    Therapy, 24, 27, 34, 43, 142-148
Sensory-tonic field theory, 29

Social economic class (SES), 3, 36, 112, 122, 126, 128
Soft signs, 1
Southern California Postrotary Nystagmus Test, 41, 81, 144
Southern California Sensory Integration Test, 41, 97, 105, 110
Subcortical, 20
Subject selection, 35

Target test, 118-119, 135-138, 151
Tonic labyrinthine reflex, 67
Tonic neck reflex, 47, 52, 61, 129
    Asymmetric (ATNR), 15, 17, 47-50, 98, 106, 124
    Symmetric (STNR), 47-51

Underlining test, 117-119, 135, 138, 151
Utricle, 69, 77-78

Vestibular, 20-25, 69, 79, 125
    Ocular-motor split, 30, 70
    Proprioceptive dissociation, 30, 70
    Dysfunction, 121, 125, 148, 150

Visually guided prehension, 5, 13, 124

Wide Range Achievement Test (WRAT), 109, 135, 138, 145, 151